STUDIES IN PHILOSOPHY
AND SCIENCE

Also by Morris R. Cohen

A PREFACE TO LOGIC
THE FAITH OF A LIBERAL

STUDIES IN PHILOSOPHY AND SCIENCE

BY MORRIS R. COHEN

NEW YORK: HENRY HOLT AND COMPANY

ACKNOWLEDGMENTS

Henry Holt and Company, Inc. and the author's son, Felix S. Cohen, are grateful for permission to reprint essays and reviews by Morris R. Cohen which originally appeared in the following publications:

"The Conception of Philosophy in Recent Discussion," *The Journal of Philosophy*, Vol. VII, 1910, p. 401.

"The Distinction Between the Mental and the Physical," *The Journal of Philosophy*, Vol. XIV, 1917, p. 261.

"Bacon and the Inductive Method," *The Scientific Monthly*, Vol. XXIII, 1926, p. 504.

"The New Realism," *The Journal of Philosophy*, Vol. X, 1913, p. 197.

"The New Realism and the Philosophy of Royce," *The Philosophical Review*, Vol. XXV, 1916, p. 378.

"Some Difficulties in John Dewey's Anthropocentric Naturalism," *The Philosophical Review*, Vol. XLIX, 1940, p. 196.

"Hegel's Rationalism," *The Philosophical Review*, Vol. XLI, 1932, p. 283 (including some material from the article on "Hegel" in the *Encyclopedia of the Social Sciences*, New York: The Macmillan Company, 1932, Vol. VII, p. 311).

"Croce and Vico," *The Philosophical Review*, Vol. XXIII, 1914, p. 677 (including some material from a review of *Le Sorgenti Irrazionali del Pensiero* by Nicola Abbagnano, in *The Journal of Philosophy*, Vol. XXI, 1924, p. 554).

"Einstein's Theory of Relativity," the *New Republic*, Vol. XXI, 1920, pp. 228, 341.

"Roads to Einstein," the *New Republic*, Vol. XXVII, 1921, p. 172.

"A Philosophy of Mathematics," *The Philosophical Review*, Vol. XXIV, 1915, p. 81.

"The Logical Foundations of the Exact Sciences," *The Journal of Philosophy*, Vol. VIII, 1911, p. 693.

"The Origins of Modern Science," *The Journal of Philosophy*, Vol. XXI, 1924, p. 456.

Also for permission to reprint essays which appeared in the following volumes:

"The Faith of a Logician," published in *Contemporary American*

Philosophy (edited by George P. Adams and William P. Montague), New York: The Macmillan Company, Vol. I, pp. 220-247.

"Belief," published in the *Encyclopedia of the Social Sciences,* New York: The Macmillan Company, 1930, Vol. II, p. 500.

CONTENTS

BOOK ONE

THE PHILOSOPHY OF SCIENCE

THE FAITH OF
A LOGICIAN

A. S. M. Amico delectissimo.

ALL AUTOBIOGRAPHY, as Goethe realized, must inevitably
contain a mixture of fiction with its truth. Our views
as to our past development cannot but be molded by our
present beliefs. But for that very reason autobiography is
one of the ways of exhibiting one's fundamental beliefs. The
assigning of motives is always a somewhat arbitrary procedure
—many conflicting ones are equally plausible. But when one
has little space to develop adequately the logical reasons
which seem to support one's main positions, it is convenient
to fall back on the form of a personal confession of faith
with an indication of the motives which led to that faith.

EDUCATION AND THE SEARCH FOR A
FUNDAMENTAL PRINCIPLE

IF PHILOSOPHY is viewed broadly as the love of wisdom or
general knowledge, I may say that such a love was awakened
in me between my seventh and tenth year by my grandfather,
a poor tailor in the Russian town of Nesviesh. Though he
never learned to write and had only a moderate reading
knowledge of Hebrew, he had become the master of an ex-
traordinary amount of knowledge and wisdom. Walks and
talks with him first stimulated my imagination about the
world at large and its history. From him, also, I acquired a
certain ineradicable admiration for the ascetic virtues and a
scorn for the life of wealth, ease, creature comforts, and all
that goes under the old name of worldliness.

For the rest I had a rather varied education. I began, like
other orthodox Hebrew boys, with the Bible, and then went

[3]

on to the Talmud. The first nonreligious book which I read was a Hebrew copy of Josephus. When, in 1890, I was sent back to live with my mother in the larger city of Minsk, I began to read Yiddish books on Hebrew history and soon drifted into very secular romances. In 1892 I was brought to New York, and in 1895 I entered the scientific course of its City College, where, in addition to mathematics, physics, chemistry, and biology, I learned to appreciate French literature.

Possibly the circumstances of my youth, which prevented me from participating in the usual boyish games, emphasized my inclination to indulge in idle or disinterested speculation. In any case, my own limited experience is in accord with the Aristotelian view that philosophy grows out of our native curiosity or wonder about the world at large. To philosophize has always seemed to me as natural and desirable in itself as to sing, to dance, to paint or mold, or to commune with those we love.

Nevertheless, the specific occasion which led me into technical philosophy was my interest in the Socialist Labor Party. Wishing to prepare ourselves for more active and intelligent propaganda, a small group of us, young college students, read Marx's *Das Kapital* and other socialist classics. The references in Marx and Engels to Hegel's dialectic method gripped me most emphatically. My courses in logic and economics at college had led me to J. S. Mill, and I felt that the fundamental issue between individualism and socialism was inextricably bound up with the difference between the psychologic and inductive method represented by Mill and the dialectic and historical method of Marx and Engels. Not having any competent guide to philosophy, I naïvely turned to Hegel himself and tried to get enlightenment from an English translation of the third part of the *Logic*. This, of course, was too tough a diet for a philosophic babe. Yet I could not abandon the quest. I had a vague conviction that there was something radically wrong with Mill's doctrine of induction and his attempt to build up a world out of independent things, facts, or "states of mind." After all, somehow or other, things *are* intimately connected in the same universe and indeed they often fuse their very being. Though I could not grasp the exact force of Hegel's argument, it became associated in my mind with Shelley's lines:

> Nothing in the world is single,
> All things by a law divine
> In one spirit meet and mingle.

My search for more definite enlightenment along this line led me to the Neo-Hegelian school; and the books which afforded me most food for reflection were Watson's *Comte, Mill and Spencer,* and Dewey's *Psychology.* They confirmed my aversion for the positivists and for their superficial efforts to dispose of the problems of reality. Yet I could not accept the constructive claims of the Neo-Hegelian philosophy. I had a strong repugnance to a certain vague, supernatural element in it that is incompatible with the spirit of the natural sciences, which have always seemed to me man's supreme achievement in the way of solid knowledge. The intellectual world was thus divided for me into two camps, and I could not be at peace in either. I therefore fell into a slough of philosophic despond from which desultory reading and agonized efforts at original thought could not extricate me.

In the spring of 1899 I gained the friendship of Thomas Davidson. His personal affection and his touchingly unrestrained faith in my abilities increased my zest in life and in philosophic study. He aroused in me the great dream of a group of congenial spirits co-operating to create a philosophic encyclopedia that should do for the culture of the twentieth century what the Brothers of Sincerity did for the Saracen culture of the tenth or what Bayle, D'Alembert, and Diderot did for the culture of the eighteenth century. My heart was thus set on the systematic and comprehensive aspect of philosophy and I was led to read generally along diverse lines.

With the poverty of time and energy at my disposal then, and for many years thereafter, the distension of my interests filled my intellectual life with many enterprises that just fell short of completion.

Davidson himself, at that time, held to an extreme subjectivism and individualism which neither gratitude nor personal admiration could induce me to accept. At his suggestion I turned from the problems of socialism and metaphysics to the problem of knowledge as dealt with by Hume and Kant. The reading of Hume left me with a profound admiration for the clarity and honesty of his skepticism as to various metaphysical and religious dogmas; but in addition to being a little irritated by that genial Tory's attitude to the rational principles of moral and political reform, his fundamental position seemed to me to involve flat contradictions. If the mind is assumed to know its own impressions only it cannot logically know that there is an external world that produces or causes these impressions. The relation between such an external world and the impressions of the mind certainly does not conform to Hume's own description of causality as the habitual succession of impressions *in* our mind. The contradiction between the practical certainty and the theoretic skepticism as to the existence of the external world (expressed at the end of the first book of Hume's Treatise) seemed to me to arise only because he had assumed both that the mind knows nothing but its own impressions and that we also know that our individual mind is only one among other objects in the universe. Obviously, if the second assumption is true, the first is false; and as the assumption of the existence of the larger world is involved in our very discussion, the mind cannot be limited to a knowledge of its own impressions only. That which is known is always more than the mere (subjective) knowing activity itself—else there could be no present recognition of past thoughts.

The effort to understand Kant's solution to Hume's problem was interrupted at that time by the necessity of helping to organize and, after Davidson's death in 1900, to continue the practical educational work which he hoped to develop into a Breadwinner's College. For a number of years I thus conducted classes in cultural history, in which I tried to apply the evolutionary philosophy to the history of industry, of the family, of religion, and of Greek and Hebrew literature. The reading of some of Professor Boas' anthropologic writings, however, soon raised doubts as to the adequacy of any formula of universal evolution, whether Hegelian or Spencerian. The discovery that our histories always depend upon our assumption as to the nature of the things studied, led me to reject the prevalent illusion that the history or temporal genesis of anything can enable us to dispense with the direct study or analysis of its present or permanent nature. The history of labor, marriage, and religion, while extending my vista, offered me no solution of their contemporary problems. Historicism, as well as psychologism, were thus ruled out for me as all-sufficient philosophic methods or as substitutes for direct rational and metaphysical analysis. In this I was strengthened by the study of Aristotle, begun in the Davidson Society and continued for two years under Professor Woodbridge. Studies in ethics under Professor Felix Adler also brought me back to my original conviction—to wit, that the problems of individual and social ethics were honeycombed with metaphysical assumptions.

It was the study of Russell's *Principles of Mathematics,* some months after I was appointed to teach mathematics at City College, that finally liberated me from the feeling of helpless philosophic bewilderment and enabled me to undertake an independent journey. The demonstration that pure mathematics asserts only logical implications and that such logical implications or relations cannot be identified with either psychologic or physical events, but are involved as determinants of both, seemed to me to offer a well-grounded and fruitful starting point for philosophy. For whatever the opinions of philosophers, they must rely on the validity of logical reasoning to establish their position; and at no time could I take seriously any attempt to question the fruitfulness of mathematical method in building up scientific knowledge. This renewed faith in logic and mathematics showed me how to avoid both the Scylla of Mill's inductive empiricism and the Charybdis of Hegelian absolutism. An inadequate view of the reality of relations or abstract universals still seems to me the common vice of both these influential philosophies. (1) Empiricism (the modern name for nominalism) never seemed to me to account for the real connections in the world. How can relations, if they exist in the mind only, connect things external to it? Moreover what can we say about any fact or thing that does not involve abstractions as determinations? (2) Similarly does the Hegelian denial of the reality of abstractions lead to the location of connections not in an objective nature but in an absolute totality that is beyond understanding. While such an absolute totality may be an ideal demand of thought, its content is always something of which we are most ignorant. Nothing is therefore really explained by it.

The doctrine that abstract logical or mathematical relations are real justified for me the hypothetico-deductive procedure of science in which we follow the implications or effects of one single aspect or factor of a situation. For not all things that occur together are relevant to each other. Scientific search is difficult just because of the exuberant multiplicity of existential coincidences which are irrelevant to our inquiry as to the order of meaning. But if scientific inquiry is successful it discovers abstract relations which do characterize the world of phenomena. Thus instead of the alternative of either swallowing the whole universe or starving intellectually, the method of logical realism showed me how to bite into it.

In subsequent reflection this metaphor of "biting into the world" proved itself peculiarly apt in suggesting that opposing considerations must be taken into account in explaining anything, and indeed that nothing is definite apart from both of every pair of polar categories such as form and matter, identity and difference, mediacy and immediacy, etc. The reality of mathematical relations, and the principle of polarity, opened for me the path to systematic philosophy.

LOGICAL REALISM

THE DISCOVERY of the logical or hypothetical character of pure mathematics showed me in a new and clear light the relation of scientific method to induction, to skepticism, and to *a priori* rationalism. This led me to a better understanding of the old and fundamental issue of conceptualism (or subjectivism) vs. realism.

Mill's contention that the truths of mathematics were approximations or inductions from experience became impossible after the distinction had been drawn between physics as a science of existence and pure mathematics as the development of the logical implications of *all* kinds of assumptions. That there are no two rational numbers whose ratio is $\sqrt{2}$ or π, is not and cannot be an induction from experience. Experience alone cannot prove the absolute impossibility of things that have not as yet occurred.

This disposed of the absolutistic nihilism (which may call itself empiricism, relativism, or skepticism) that denies the existence of all necessary truths and tries to maintain that even propositions like "2 plus 2 equals 4" are contingent so that on some other planet the result might be different. One does not have to go to another planet to see that two pints of water and two pints of alcohol will not necessarily make four pints of the mixture. But the hypothetical truths of pure mathematics are not affected by empirical physical facts that do not conform to its postulated conditions. The truth of the proposition that "two and two equals four" (assuming the usual definitions and postulates of arithmetic) is not a question of physical observation, nor of psychologic habit, but

[9]

of logical proof. It can be demonstrated that its denial involves self-contradiction, and thus cannot maintain itself. It cannot, therefore, be true that all assertions are merely personal opinions; or if you call them opinions, it is certainly true that the opinion "2 plus 2 equals 5" is not as true as "2 plus 2 equals 4."

However, the same realization of the logical and hypothetical nature of pure mathematics also destroyed classical *a priori* rationalism. It destroyed the ground of any assertion that we know *a priori* and with apodeictic certainty that physical space must be Euclidean, just as the development of modern physics has rendered vain Kant's further argument that we know *a priori* that physical nature must follow Newtonian laws of mechanics. Indeed, renewed faith in formal logic showed me that since all proof rests on assumption, it is vain for any philosophy to pretend to prove all of its material propositions. It must make indemonstrable assumptions in regard to existence, value, or duty. This is particularly cogent against Kant's transcendental method, i.e., the attempt to prove certain propositions true because they explain how experience is possible. We cannot explain experience or anything else without assuming something; and it is a downright logical fallacy to assert that because our assumptions explain something they are therefore demonstrably true. Obviously Kant does not and cannot offer any cogent proof that there may not be some other set of assumptions which will also explain the facts of experience.

That an assumption is not proved is, of course, not an argument against its truth. So long also as assumptions differ there will be ground for preferring the one that best explains the assumed facts. But the recognition of possible alternative assumptions bankrupts the pretension that philosophic assertions are all necessary and not merely probable truths. Doctrines as to the material nature of the world or of our duties in it can thus never be more than merely probable.

The principles or laws of every science are the rules or

constant relations which hold amidst all the changes in its field; and so the fundamental laws or postulates of pure mathematics or logic are the invariant forms or relations which hold of all possible objects.[1] Logical laws are thus neither physical nor mental but the laws of all possible significant being. No material fact can be deduced from purely formal considerations, but formal relations are assumed in inferring any fact from any others, and indeed no fact can be formulated except in terms of the forms or universal relations embodied in it. The world which is the object of science (since all science involves logic) is thus a union of form and matter. It is rational in the sense that its phenomena do conform to the laws of possibility that are the objects of logic; but the element of chance or contingency can never be eliminated from it, since all proof must rest on unproved assumptions. The world may also be said to contain an irrational element in the sense that all form is the form of something which cannot be reduced to form alone. The duality or polarity of terms and relations cannot be eliminated by reducing everything to terms alone, or to relations alone. We may say that everything which is intelligible can be expressed in logical form; but that which is expressible has no valid claim to absolute totality. Nor is there any contradiction in speaking of the inexpressible, since it is of the essence of all expression to point to something beyond itself.

THE PRINCIPLE OF POLARITY

THE PRINCIPLE of polarity is suggested by the phenomena of magnetism where north and south pole are always distinct, opposed, yet inseparable. We can see it in general physics where there is no action without reaction, no force or cause

[1] I have tried to show this in greater detail in *The Journal of Philosophy*, Vol. VIII (1911), pp. 533 ff., and Vol. XV (1918), p. 673, republished in *Reason and Nature* (1931), p. 171, and *A Preface to Logic* (1944), p. 1.

of change without inertia or resistance. In biology the life of every organism involves action and reaction with an environment. There is no growth without decay, or as Huxley puts it, protoplasm manages to live only by continually dying. This suggests a supplement to the principle of causality. Not only must every natural event have a cause which determines that it should happen, but the cause must be opposed by some factor which prevents it from producing any greater effect than it actually does. A physical or chemical system has the precise rate of change that it has, an organism attains its specific form at any moment, a social movement has just the effect or influence which it in fact has, because of the presence of certain opposing or balancing factors necessary to produce the definite result.

From this point of view not only every static, but also every kinetic, system involves a balance or equilibrium which makes description in the form of equations applicable. Of course it is only when the elements are measurable and thus numerically formulated that equations can generally be employed in a fruitful way. But it should be noted (1) that exact or mathematical reasoning is not restricted to quantity, but is applicable in nonquantitative realms like group theory or analysis situs, and (2) that quantitative determination is but one way of eliminating the indetermination of such descriptions as A is hot, A is cold, A is large, A is small, etc. Statements such as A is 60° F. or 5 yds. include the truth of opposite partial statements, and assert something definite and determinate in relation to all comparable objects.

The principle of polarity, of necessary opposition in all determinate effects, thus becomes a heuristic principle directing our inquiry in the search for adequate explanations. Hence, if we pass from the realm of natural events, where reigns the principle of causality, to the wider realm of all possible objects of consideration governed by the principle of sufficient reason, our principle of polarity becomes a supplement to the latter. It then asserts that in all determination there are opposing elements or categories, such as unity and plurality, identity and difference, activity and passivity.

The obvious value of the principle of polarity is in enabling us to avoid one-sided and interminable (because indeterminate) issues, and in making us more hospitable to the complexity of seemingly paradoxical facts such as that we rest alternately on our feet while walking or that we remain the same while growing or changing. All this is of the utmost importance in metaphysics or general philosophy where we are subject to two great temptations: (1) to hasty generalization about objects like the universe which are not as determinate as is commonly supposed, and (2) to deny the vision of others who see things from a different point of view.

(1) The question of the indeterminateness of the absolute or total universe will occupy us later. At present it is well to note that while reality has many elements and everything is held in place by opposite forces working at the same time, our thought and expression is linear, i.e., we think and write along one line at a time.

(2) That the great philosophers are generally right in what they assert (of their own vision) and wrong in what they deny (of the vision of others) was recognized by Leibniz. In any case we must be both critical and sympathetic toward the philosophy of others, and avoid both the blindness of excessive partisanship and the mushiness of eclecticism typified by those soapy minds that, when confronted by the choice between heaven and hell, hope to combine the good points of each.

The effort to eliminate false alternatives or one-sided views is characteristic of the Hegelian philosophy. Yet the principle of polarity is not the same as that of the Hegelian dialectic. In the first place the distinction between the formal and the material, between logical categories and historical existences, removes the Hegelian confusion in which concrete things seem to be generated in time either by ghostly conflicts or by sublimated matings of abstract categories. Novelty in

[1 3]

concrete being cannot be generated by the combination of pure abstract forms. This objection may be taking Hegel's metaphors too literally; but the confusion needs to be eliminated in any case. In the second place, the principle of polarity leads to a more emphatic denial of identity between opposite categories like being and nonbeing. The opposition between contrary categories is neither absorbed nor in any way transcended by their unity, any more than abstract unity can be generated by abstract difference. The opposing considerations involved in all existences (like the north and south pole of a magnet) are different aspects which never become identical though they necessarily coexist. Nor does the fact that they are only phases of concrete existences make them in any significant sense unreal. (We can, of course, define the real as that which exists only as concrete; but then the proposition that the abstract is not in this sense real becomes a mere tautology.)

So long as significant wholes involve diverse parts, the latter are to the scientific vision just as real or valid as the former. On the other hand, since absolute totality is an ideal limit in some respects never actually attained, the parts are psychologically more real or vivid than the whole. If abstractions are parts of any possibly existing world, statements about these parts need not be false. Partial truths are not simply false; for in the effort to attain truth, false statements must be eliminated, but partial truths need only to be supplemented.

The principle of sufficient reason on which we rely doubtless postulates a world in which different things are more or less connected. But the ideal totality does not exist in nature at any one time nor even as any actuality of knowledge. It is a necessary ideal to indicate the direction of our scientific effort, but it cannot serve as an explanation of any particular thing in it.

Under the head of polarities we may distinguish between contradictions, antinomies, and aporias or difficulties. Strictly speaking, contradictions are always dialectical, i.e., they hold only in a logical universe. Thus, if I say a house is thirty years old, and someone else says it is thirty-one years old, the two statements are contradictory in the sense that both cannot possibly be true at the same time and in the same respect. Both statements, however, can certainly be true if we draw a distinction, e.g., thirty-one years since the beginning and thirty years since the completion of its building.

Thus, two statements which, taken abstractly, are contradictory may both be true of concrete existence provided they can be assigned to separate domains or aspects. A plurality of aspects is an essential trait of things in existence. Determinate existence thus continues free from self-contradiction because there is a distinction between the domains in which these opposing statements are each separately true. When opposing statements are completed by reference to the domains wherein they are true, there is no logical difficulty in combining them. In the purely logical or mathematical field, however, we deal not with complexes of existence, but with abstract determinations as such. Here two contradictory assertions always produce a resultant which is zero, i.e., the entity of which they are asserted is absolutely impossible.

Of incompletely determined existence—as in the case of the total universe—contradictory propositions do not annihilate each other (since they refer to a complex of existences); and yet they cannot always (because of the indefiniteness of the subject) be reconciled with each other. This gives rise to the antinomies of metaphysics.

In general, the opposite statements that are true in regard to existing things give rise to difficulties when we cannot see how to draw the proper distinction which will enable us to reconcile and combine these seeming contradictions. Thus, we frequently find certain facts in a scientific realm calling for one theory, e.g., the corpuscular theory of light, and other facts calling for a diametrically opposite one, viz., the wave theory. Such difficulties are solved either by discovering new facts, which give one of these theories a preponderance, or else by discovering a way of combining the two theories. Sometimes an intellectual dilemma is avoided by rejecting both alternatives. This is illustrated by the old difficulty as to whether language was a human invention or a special revelation. The difficulty was avoided by introducing the concept of natural growth.

Nature also presents us with seeming impossibilities in the form of practical difficulties, e.g., how to live long without getting old, how to eat our cake and yet have it too, etc. Such contingent or physical impossibilities may baffle us forever. Yet some of them may be solved by finding the proper distinction. Thus the invention of boats enabled us to eliminate a former impossibility—namely, how to cross a river without getting wet.

This analysis puts us on guard against two opposite evil intellectual habits: on the one hand to regard real difficulties as absolute impossibilities, and on the other to belittle such difficulties by calling them false alternatives. Thus it is not sufficient to say that the old controversy between the claims of the active and those of the contemplative life represents a false alternative and that we need both. It is, in fact, most frequently impossible to follow both, and the actual problem of how much of one we need to sacrifice to the other often requires more knowledge than is at our disposal.

THE UNIVERSE AS AN ABSOLUTE TOTALITY

THE FACT that we can speak of the universe and can refer to *it* naturally inclines us to emphasize its unity. It is, however, possible to speak of a heap of things that have no bond except that of being together in a given space. Whether the universe, as the totality of all things actual and possible, has a greater unity than a merely spatial one, we are, in view of the fragmentary character of our knowledge, in no position to answer. We do not even know with certainty whether the universe includes a finite or an infinite number of material particles. Because of its essential incompleteness we can form no definite image of it.

The universe cannot be made definite by distinguishing it from something outside of it. Nor can it be made complete and definite by showing the order or pattern which prevails through it, since all sorts of incompatible patterns and lack of order are also found in it. The universe is obviously not completely or actually in existence at any one time. It contains many abstract possibilities which are not physically compossible, so that when some of them are realized, others become impossible. If the chaos of illusions and contradictory possibilities are said to exist in the mind only, they are not thereby banished from the universe, since the mind exists in it; and if we define existence in such a way that illusions are said not to exist, all illusions will not be thereby eliminated. The realm of existence may by definition be restricted to some orderly cosmos, but the universe will continue to include many other things besides. This indefiniteness in what is denoted by the term *universe,* as an absolute totality without qualification, makes all sorts of contrary propositions true of it.

The universe is neither given in experience nor is it a mental construction; yet it is certainly in some sense given. The totality of all things is obviously not given in sense perception. What is so given is always something occupying some part of time and space. Obviously, the total universe includes more than we can ever perceive or form into an image. Our experiences taper off into the indefinite, but in any case no finite number of them can give us an absolute totality. Neither can the universe be a mental construction. The extent and complexity of the world is beyond our power of synthesis. We cannot think of all the possible relations of even a finite number of entities, and the number of possible qualifications of our world is endless. Yet it is impossible to maintain that nothing at all exists, or to deny that there is a world in some sense or other.

[17]

Out of this and similar dilemmas, we can extricate ourselves only by recognizing that "the world" is a symbol for something not completely determinate. It is partly known but also always involves the unknown. Any part of the latter may become known, but never the whole of it. Part of the universe exists, but many more parts do not. Many parts of the universe are determined, but so long as plurality, individuality, and novelty are not denied, contingency or indetermination is unelminable. Part of the universe is material and part is mental. But any assertion that all is matter or that all is mind amounts to a violent resolution to use an old word in a new and confusing way to include its negative. For consider the difference between the house we live in and the house we dream of. Whether you say both are material or both are mental, the factual difference remains and is accounted for by neither of the monistic assertions about the universe.

Similar antinomies hold with regard to the assertion that the universe is changing and that it remains identical. Stated positively the universe is an ideal, in the sense that it indicates the direction in which the full nature of things is to be found. It is present formally, not actually. As present it includes all unreality, illusion, etc., which in a certain sense do form the content of the world, even if we define existence to exclude them as unreal.

PHILOSOPHY OF NATURE

THE TWO POLES of philosophic interests are the macroscopic and the microscopic, the infinite totality of everything (*the* universe), and the ultimate elements which enter into anything. Logicians may be most passionately interested in the larger vistas, but a faith in truth similar to that of Browning's Grammarian makes them devote themselves to the minuter problems.

Is the world one or many? Both the continuity and discreteness of things stare us in the face; and monists and pluralists differ because they fail to do justice to both of these aspects of nature. Since every proposition (A is B) involves elements that are different and yet in some way identical, there is no hope for philosophy unless it recognizes that identity and difference while logically different are existentially inseparable in the nature of anything. The classical philosophers, impressed by the logic of identity, naturally belittled the importance of change which introduces diversity into the nature of the things that change. Modernistic philosophers stress the fact of change so as to ignore those elements of unity or identity without which things cannot be said to change. Common sense is shocked by the idea of change without anything that changes; and logic reconciles change and constancy by saying that the nature of anything is the group of invariant relations which remain the same throughout the change.

As a result of the progress of modern physics and biology many of the formerly assumed constancies of nature, like the eternity of the hills or the fixity of species, have disappeared. But science has also discovered invariable order in changes which formerly seemed chaotic and arbitrary.

If change is essential to the constitution of natural or temporal objects it follows that they cannot be adequately described in terms of what they actually or sensibly are at any moment. The actual dominates us sensibly and vitally, but it is only an infinitesimal part of the larger world of possibilities. The nature of anything must include its possibilities. The danger of taking possibilities seriously, however, is that of thinking of them as if they were thin copies or ghosts of actual things floating in space.

The fact that things change according to some order gives rise to the ideas of determinism and causality. But if anything is to be affected by something else, it must be distinct from that other. It must, then, have a realm which is not due to or affected by that other. A genuinely pluralistic world cannot be completely determined in all respects. The general impression that the discovery of laws by the natural sciences rules out the element of chance or contingency from our world is shown to be erroneous by these considerations:

1. The most thoroughgoing mechanism necessarily involves contingent data. If you derive the present arrangement of particles in the universe from a previous one by assuming some law, you push back the contingency to the past arrangement. Mechanical forces cannot be supposed to operate except on a given distribution of material particles. The contingency of such distribution is as ultimate as the existence of the assumed laws.

2. Every physical law asserts that a certain phenomenon or characteristic of it depends on a limited number of factors and on nothing else. There is no use in saying that temperature and pressure determine the freezing point, if the latter depends upon everything else. Every law of dependence thus implies independence of all other things, which are thus irrelevant to the given effect.

3. The ultimate laws of nature are themselves contingent. They just happen to be. Any one law or reason from which they might all be derived (which is logically impossible) would itself be contingent, without any proof that it might not have been different. An infinite regress cannot eliminate contingency, and the existence of a different world is always a theoretically significant alternative.

The insistence that the search for scientific law presupposes elements of independence as well as dependence in nature, aids us against vicious forms of atomism, organicism, and mysticism. Atomism is vicious if it makes every entity a complete and independent universe, in disregard of its relations to other entities. We see such vicious atomism in individualistic anarchism and in pleas for irresponsible self-expression. Vicious organicism is the refusal to note any relative independence or externality of relations between things which happen to be juxtaposed in our universe. It shows itself in the persistent tendency to confuse every line of clear thought by appeal to a vague totality which is irrelevant to the point at issue. Mysticism is vicious or obscurantist if it denies the definite or determinate character of things in the interest of beliefs that cannot stand the light of reason.

TELEOLOGY AND VITALISM

THE BELIEF that independence, contingency, and spontaneity in nature are not inconsistent with genuine laws or invariant relations (strengthened in me by the writings of C. S. Peirce) does not justify the use of final causes by vitalists to deny the scientific fruitfulness of physico-chemical explanations in biology. It is perfectly legitimate to describe organic and even inorganic phenomena from the point of view of the consequent so that the antecedent seems a means. But we must be on guard against attributing conscious effort and intention to nature when there is no adequate evidence for their actual existence. It is tempting to describe the behavior of organisms in terms of self-preservation; but it is equally legitimate to describe the life of every individual as a successful effort to attain death. The circulation of the blood in the human body is one of the necessary conditions of its consciousness, but consciousness is not a necessary condition for the circulation of the blood. Most of the arguments used by Driesch, Bergson, and other vitalists against possible progress in the physical explanation of biologic facts seem to me demonstrably erroneous. But at best they would only prove that in regard to certain phases of life we must remain in ignorance. Bergson's attempts to explain specific biologic phenomena (such as the supposed similarity of structure between the eye of the scallop and the vertebrate eye) by means of "life as a whole," conflicts with the rule of scientific method that specific effects must be explained by specific causes. Nor will the hypothetical "psychoids" and similar entities of Driesch and others, stand the test of scientific verification. The phenomena of life are assuredly different from those of nonliving nature; but there is no proof that life did not arise (or may not now be arising) out of nonliving material. And there is no good reason why the scientific methods which have proved fruitful in the inorganic sciences should not be tried in the field of biology. Popular teleologic evolutionism, in which man appears at the top of a biologic ladder that all other organisms are trying to mount, seems to me romantic vanity. That many species—indeed all vertebrates—have originated in simpler forms seems historically clear. But there is no law of evolution that all organisms must change in a given direction. Indeed experimental biology does not need the concept of evolution at all. When it clings to it, it is only out of verbal piety.

The study of biology should also impress us with the discontinuity of nature. For without such discontinuity we could not recognize different species.

MIND AND BODY

THE REJECTION, in my youth, of the whole supernatural world-view left no room for the mind or soul as an entity existing apart from the body. I have never been able to imagine what mental life apart from any body can possibly be. All sensations, feelings, emotions, etc., seem to me to be events in a body, and to involve consciousness of that body. If, then, the rejection of the belief in ghosts or disembodied spirits be materialism, I should call myself a materialist like Democritus, Hobbes, and Spinoza. Such materialism makes me reject the fundamental assumption of Freud and others who talk of purely mental determinism. Mental life is spasmodic and interrupted so that it lacks the continuity for the direct application of the causal relation. It is doubtless true that worry and other emotions will have serious bodily effects. But the cause of these bodily effects can be found in the bodily accompaniments of the emotions. It is therefore only in a popular and practical, but not in a scientifically accurate, sense that we can speak of the mind as exerting efficient causality. The sense of mental efficiency is an indication of vitality. But the laws of causality operate just as truly when we are not mentally very efficient.

I must emphatically reject the view of those materialists or behaviorists who think that the existence of conscious phenomena can be denied or adequately described in purely physical terms. Consciousness, when it happens, is a real addition to the phenomena of nature. It is unlike anything else. How it originates and what sustains it seem to me to be empirical and not metaphysical questions.

The popular notion that materialism has been refuted by the theory that atoms are composed of electrons seems to me rather fatuous. Natural science must remain materialistic in the sense that it must always reject explanations of material phenomena in terms of disembodied spirits or other unverifiable entities.

The form of materialism that is objectionable to science and which has been refuted by philosophers since Plato is that of nominalism, which denies the reality of relations or logical connection between things. For purposes of certain analyses it is convenient to regard matter as entirely inert; but reflection shows that a material world must necessarily involve some spontaneity; and there is no *a priori* reason why life and mind may not develop in it. All we need to remember is that our conception of the material world must include the possibility of such development.

Mind is often considered, not as a natural existence or function of an individual organism, but abstractly, as when we speak of the mind of an age or nation. We thus speak of science as a spiritual body to which different individuals contribute. As a natural existence, however, science appears as a complex of books, apparatus, the memories of individual organisms, etc.

[23]

ETHICS

FROM A NATURALISTIC POINT of view the whole life of the human species is a minor episode in the history of a tiny speck of cosmic dust; and man's natural fate is determined by forces which visit death and destruction upon the just and the unjust. Yet logically the problem of ethics is just as legitimate as the problem of physics. In both cases we may be said to begin with a set of primitive judgments—in the first case that certain things exist and in the second case that they are good or ought to be. We deal with these judgments scientifically if we examine them critically and elaborate them in the form of a rational system determined by principles. The greater difficulties of a theory of ethics are due to the greater variability of man's moral judgments and their dependence on all sorts of conventions which differ according to time and place. Diverse peoples who agree in condemning murder, incest, theft, etc., as immoral do not necessarily mean the same thing by these terms. Christians who accept the command "thou shalt not kill," do not think it wrong to kill at the command of a military officer. Few see anything wrong in long-distance killing, e.g., in our starving other peoples like the Chinese by monopolizing the fertile lands that keep us in luxury. The Old Testament horror of incest does not touch Abraham's marrying his half sister.

Moral feelings are very strong, but this does not prevent them from appearing as irrational taboos to those who do not share our conventions. This should warn us against the tendency to make ethical philosophy an apology or justification of the conventional customs that happen to be established. Suppose that someone were to offer our country a wonderfully convenient mechanism, but demand in return the privilege of killing thousands of our people every year. How many of those who would indignantly refuse such a request will condemn the use of the automobile now that it is already with us?

On the other hand, there can be no moral appeal except to some desire that persists. The most rabid amoralist like Nietzsche must appeal to his reader's sense as to what is desirable; and the followers of Karl Marx, who boasted that he never spoke of justice, would be dumb and ineffective if they could not appeal to a hatred for the injustice of our present economic order.

These reflections lead me to the rejection, not only of the Hebrew idea of moral laws as commands of Yahveh, but also the Kantian view of specific moral rules (such as that against lying) as absolute or categorical imperatives. It leads me to the Aristotelian conception of ethical judgments as matters of wisdom in the conduct of life. Specific ethical rules are lessons as to what is good, illumined by past experience and therefore subject to correction and revision. This saves us from fanaticism and such hideous insensibility as is involved in Kant's condemnation of a lie told to save an innocent life from a foul murder. The naturalistic view of morals also carries with it a greater regard for natural desires. The moral life must, to be sure, be one of discipline and self-restraint, if like any other art it is to achieve anything. Restraints on natural impulses are, however, good only if, like the restraints on public traffic, they make possible a greater freedom and a maximum of natural satisfaction of our heart's desire. At the same time I cannot completely accept hedonism. The virtues of the hero and the martyr point to the incommensurability of certain moral values, and this offers insuperable difficulties to any calculus of pleasures. Nor can I accept indiscriminate altruism or love of humanity as an adequate principle of all moral life. It is neither possible to love all mankind—I cannot love my neighbor's wife and children as my own—nor would it be good to do so. We can only love what is lovable; and the philosopher must not forget that everything that is morally vile arises out of human nature.

If all our natural impulses were good, all training and education would be needless restraint and evil. But the impulses of men and women to direct the conduct of their children and to train them in certain ways are themselves natural, and it is vain to try to suppress them in the interests of unrestrained naturalness.

The truth is that our nature is full of deadly tendencies and that the life of culture or civilization is wisdom organized to combat natural evil. Often, indeed, such organization misses its objective and adds to the burden of life so that some return to simplicity is necessary. But the life of reason is developed by civilization and is not compatible with a return to a purely animal status.

PHILOSOPHY OF LAW

HUMAN BEINGS cannot live together without restraints on their anarchic impulses. Yet, if laws are to be effective, these restraints must appeal to the community. This difficulty is solved by general obedience to a ruler or rule. In modern societies the rule of law is relied on more and more to eliminate the arbitrary personal bias of rulers and to make men more certain as to what are their rights and what they may safely undertake. But philosophic pluralism makes us distrust rules; for the latter are based on generalizations as to what takes place in a dominant number, but not in all cases, so that rules always work hardships in individual cases whose peculiarities are not anticipated by the rule. Many things must therefore be left to the intuition, tact, or good judgment of well-disposed and competent judges or other officials. There can be no government by law apart from men who will administer the law according to their ideas and feelings. How can we guard against the arbitrary and tyrannical abuse of such discretion? Yet, discretion or judgment, if it is sound, embodies some reason or rule which subsequent study may make clear.

[26]

My interest in this field was first stimulated by the course of judicial decisions in labor cases. The arbitrary (and often unenlightened) character of these decisions revealed to me the inadequacy of the dogma that judges declare but do not make the law. The rejection of the absoluteness of this distinction between making and finding threw light on the issue between realism and idealism, as to whether the mind makes or discovers the nature of the world.

The unsatisfactory character of American judicial decisions in labor cases led me to question the value and adequacy of the moral principles of the American Bill of Rights which form the justification of these decisions. "Equal protection of law" seems highly desirable in the abstract, but in its application to actual unequal individuals it turns out to be most vague and unsatisfactory. But my aversion to positivism, to the position of those who, like Duguit, claim to reject the strictly ethical or normative point of view, led me to see the truth in the old doctrine of natural law and natural rights. The moral demand that law should answer to man's interests cannot be ignored in the study or in the making of the law; and the evaluation of these interests is thus an integral part of any philosophy of law.

Law, and even the ethical ideal itself, may certainly be viewed as the historic resultant of various social forces. Yet the old problem of natural law, the problem as to what under given conditions the law ought to be, remains. Realism in the law can be combined with genuine idealism in the doctrine of the inherent limitations of legal idealism due to the conditions of human nature, habits, the legal machinery, and the limitations of man's desire for the moral good.

PHILOSOPHY OF ART

MY GENERAL INCLINATION to naturalistic rationalism was fortified by the discovery that it seemed to be the most satisfactory account of a field to which it is seldom applied—to wit, the field of art.

The ascetic and democratic ideas with which I began to philosophize predisposed me to view aestheticism as a form of snobbery. That which has its roots deep in human nature, or answers to our fundamental needs, cannot depend upon acquaintance with rare paintings or esoteric music. Reflection, however, on the fact that only a few who are highly trained understand the meaning of such scientific laws as that of gravitation, suggested that in the field of art, too, training may make clear what is otherwise vague and indistinct. This led to a distinction between taste which is immediate and vision which involves discrimination in the object seen. If taste denotes mere sensibility there seems little basis for saying that where two tastes differ one is necessarily superior to the other. A pluralistic philosophy finds plenty of anthropologic evidence for the view that talk about superior taste may mean a blindness to its natural diversity. The terms *higher* and *lower* have a meaning only in regard to things of the same kind that can be arranged in a linear series. But on what basis can one declare that a taste for Da Vinci's faces is superior to a taste for Turner's landscapes, or either to a taste for Japanese prints? If anyone is justified in saying that it is poor taste to prefer jazz to Beethoven, it can only be either on the ground that those who prefer the latter are "better" people or else because the objective content or structure of Beethoven's music shows greater art than does jazz. This means a consideration of art rather than mere taste.

If we look on the fine arts as a special group of arts we can see that the problem of creation which they involve is ultimately the rational one of adapting means to ends.[2] To be sure the end is not always clear at the beginning, but becomes

[2] This means that intelligent art criticism must be based on a knowledge of the problems which face the artist and the technique whereby they are solved. The true critic repeats in part the intellectual work of the artist himself.

clearer as we work towards it. But this is true also in scientific research and other activities. What distinguishes the fine arts from the other arts is the character of the resulting product. (I reject the suggestion that what characterizes all activity in the fine arts is its pleasantness. Some of it may be painful and not as pleasant as certain activities in the industrial arts or in business.) The artistic product does generally please the observer (with reservations as to the sublime), but not all things which please us are the products of fine art. The latter pleases us by producing things that have a certain structure characterized by rhythm, harmony, or, more generally, beauty.

Beauty is generally viewed as an immediate attribute; but reflection shows that it also elevates us above the actual or material object which embodies it. Aristotle's dictum that poetry is more true than history, means that the artistic representation of the essence of an object has more significance than the mere recital of brute historic facts. Liberation from the actual through a suggestion of possibilities beyond it is as characteristic of art as of theoretic science and religion.

PHILOSOPHY OF RELIGION

HAVING BEEN brought up as an orthodox Hebrew, religion was first associated in my mind with cultus, with prayers and ritual observances. Study of the history of Buddhism, Christianity, and Islam confirmed the view that ritual, what men do on certain occasions, is the primary fact, and that the beliefs and emotions associated with ritual are more variable. The same prayer or ritual may have quite different emotional effects. Also many a man like Chief Justice Marshall goes to church without bothering his head about any question of belief. Robertson Smith's observation that ritual is generally older than the myth which explains it, has always impressed me as the beginning of wisdom in a rational study of religion. It is certainly profusely exemplified in the succession of diverse mythical explanations of the Hebrew Sabbath, the Easter ceremony, the worship at Mecca, etc. A Christian saint may replace the local heathen god, but people continue to worship at the same shrine.

From this point of view recent discussions of religion initiated by William James's *Varieties of Religious Experience,* seem to me singularly provincial and unilluminating. They throw no light on the main streams of human experience expressed in the great historic religions, such as Brahmanism, Buddhism, Zoroastrianism, Confucianism, etc. James's remark that the religious experience of the great mass of people is secondary, and only that of the founders is important, is certainly superficial. The character of the founder of a religion is largely a product of tradition. Gautama, Moses, and Jesus influence the religion of their followers through the ideal personality that tradition has molded. Tradition is the most powerful influence in religion. Of the hundreds of millions of people who follow the way of the Buddha, or invoke the name of Mohammed, how many do so because they were born and brought up in their respective communities? How many of those who are convinced that the supreme truth has been revealed to Moses or Jesus have examined the claims of other religions? Clearly the forces of social cohesion determine the main stream of religious phenomena. These considerations have destroyed for me the force of the argument that religion must be true because so many people believe it. As we learn more about diverse religions we find no substantial common core of dogma or belief. Neither the belief in a personal God, nor in personal immortality with moral retribution after death, is common to Old Testament Judaism, to Buddhism, and to Confucianism.

I confess that I have never been able to understand any theism that was not anthropomorphic; and I have not since my thirteenth year seen any logical force in the theistic argument that the entire universe must have a person (on the human model) as its cause, designer, or director. Any conception of personality which we can form is necessarily based upon such infinitesimal knowledge of the unimaginable whole wherein we move, that it seems to me blind arrogance to be confident of the personalistic explanation. Nor can I see how the author of our whole world can be called good, without blunting the edge of the distinction between good and evil. I do not like to call myself an atheist, because those who apply that term to themselves seem as a rule singularly blind to the limitations of our knowledge and to the infinite possibilities beyond us. As a pluralist I believe that the forces which control all things are ultimately many; and if I could use the term polytheism without implying that these forces are exclusively personal I should call myself a polytheist.

Though I am singularly sensitive to the literary charm of certain types of mysticism such as that of St. Bernard, or Tauler, it seems to me amazing that anyone should argue as James did that the mystic's ecstasy can prove any of the dogmas of religion. I can see no proof that the object of the mystic's experience has any more objective validity than the similar visions of one under the influence of drugs. Nor is the moral elevation of religious conviction beyond question. There is not a revolting feature of human life that has not at one time or another been an intimate part of religion. Sacred prostitution, the sacrifice of children to Moloch, thuggery, assassination, superstitious opposition to science, persecution and wars, the sanctification of slavery and other social abuses— these are but a few phases of religion that it is well not to forget. It may be urged that religion did not originate these practices but only sanctioned them. But if so why may not the moral and aesthetic goods often attributed to religion be similarly of independent origin? History does not support the view that the actual religions of mankind have been the source of good only.

Despite the darker side of religion, such as uncharitable beliefs in hell, I doubt not that it lifts men above mere brutish existence and saves them from the deadening absorptions of the market place. Popular religions are doctrines of hope which sustain men's faith by assuring them that the world as a whole is not indifferent to their moral strivings. I for one cannot see in history or in nature any rational proof of "a power not ourselves making for righteousness." But surely the deeper religious consciousness recognizes that moral effort justifies itself apart from rewards or outer success. Rational naturalism and the great religions are at one in impressing us with the wisdom of humility and resignation. We are not gods, and cannot mold the entire world according to our heart's desire. But we can, by learning to face the truth, attain peace and freedom from vanity. God is not only an existent power but an ideal of holiness, which enables us to distinguish between the good and the evil in men and thus saves us from the idolatrous worship of a humanity that is full of fatal imperfections. Men need not live forever or beyond the grave to attain true spirituality—to act with a view to the inherent quality of our acts and to see them as parts of the eternal web of the world.

> . . . For to bear all naked truths,
> And to envisage circumstance, all calm,
> That is the top of sovereignty.

THE CONCEPTION OF PHILOS-
OPHY IN RECENT DISCUSSION

THE SIGNIFICANCE of the conceptions of philosophy that have
been dominant in America is perhaps best understood if
they are viewed against the background of the career of philosophy since antiquity.

The term "philosophy" seems first to have been used by
Herodotus and Thucydides in its literal sense, to denote the
desire or pursuit of wisdom. The speculative bias of the
Greeks made them restrict the term "philosophy" to theoretic
knowledge only, i.e., knowledge pursued for its own sake as
opposed to that which is technical or immediately practical.
The terms "science," "true knowledge," and "philosophy"
are used almost interchangeably by Plato and Aristotle. The
idea that philosophy is not ordinary knowledge but has for
its object something of superior worth, to wit, the real as
opposed to the phenomenal, is due to the Platonic doctrine
that true knowledge can be only of the immutable and the
eternal. Aristotle also emphasizes the fact that philosophic or
scientific knowledge is reasoned or demonstrative, and, therefore, depends on knowledge of causes or principles. Though
Aristotle wrote on political and natural history he seems to
have clearly distinguished between history and science or
philosophy. Both Plato and Aristotle, while setting a high
value on mathematics, hesitated to apply the term "philosophy" to it. Thus Plato put mathematics in the borderland
between true science and opinion; and Aristotle, while explicit in his statements that metaphysics, physics, and mathematics are the three parts of theoretic philosophy, and in his
reference to metaphysics as the first, and to physics as the second, philosophy, does not explicitly refer to mathematics as
the third philosophy. Nevertheless, mathematics did not become generally dissociated from philosophy until the Alexandrine period (e.g., Euclid), and even later we find the book

[33]

of Sextus Empiricus, *Adversus Mathematicos,* directed against the philosophers or metaphysicians.

The distinction between philosophy and the special sciences was accentuated by the Stoic and the Epicurean philosophies, with their emphasis on ethics as the major portion of philosophy. In the light of the popular use of the term "philosopher" as synonymous with moral teacher or guide, and the prevailing idea of philosophy as a mode of life, pursuits like those of Archimedes could not be referred to as philosophical. At any rate, the Alexandrine period finds a number of special sciences cultivated separately from philosophy.

In medieval times, philosophy was used to denote all the knowledge which can be acquired by natural reason without the aid of revelation. In practice, this meant all the subjects treated by "the Philosopher," i.e., Aristotle; and as these formed the substance of all arts courses, the faculty of arts became known as the faculty of philosophy. The "three philosophies" denoted moral, natural, and metaphysical philosophy.

As a result of the development of natural philosophy into the independent science of physics, and the emphasis on the problems of thought or consciousness in writers like Locke, the term "metaphysics" gave way to the term "mental science" or "intellectual philosophy." As a result, also, of the expansion of modern science and its imperative demand for specialization, the parts of moral philosophy known as jurisprudence, law of nature, politics, and economics—subjects on which an eighteenth century professor of philosophy like Adam Smith was expected to lecture—soon became objects of study on the part of specialists who did not concern themselves with the rest of philosophy. For several decades empirical psychology has been assuming more and more the role of a special science, as independent of philosophy as the science of optics. In our own day there is a strong tendency for investigators in the field of logic to regard their subject as a branch of either psychology or mathematics; and an increasing number now view the field of ethics as part of sociology or anthropology.

After the special sciences have thus been carved out of it, what, if anything, is left of philosophy itself? The typical answers to this question may be arranged in three groups, between which hard and fast lines cannot be drawn:

1. Those that deny that there is any peculiar subject matter or method in philosophy. This is the view of the agnostic and nineteenth century positivist schools. To both Spencer and Comte philosophy consists simply in the unification or co-ordination of the various sciences. In Spencer this unity is a mere juxtaposition—the only bond uniting the various sciences being the fact that they all have certain vague general laws of evolution in common. In Comte the unity is one of end. In constituting the positive philosophy the various sciences are subordinated to each other in accordance with the needs of the positive polity. In harmony with this is the popular view that philosophy is simply the sum of the general portions of the different sciences.

2. Those that insist that philosophy still has a subject matter distinct from that of the special sciences, viz., the real or the rational. This group includes representatives of most diverse schools of philosophic thought, who, of course, conceive this subject matter in different ways. Thus, the Hegelian school conceives the subject matter of all philosophy to be the ultimately real, or absolute, Idea, a knowledge of which we obtain by a system of reasoning. The mystic schools all conceive the real, which is the quest of philosophy, to be in the ineffable One attained in certain experiences, called feeling or intuition. Between these two schools may be placed an influential group of thinkers like Münsterberg, Duhem, and Bergson, having little in common save the view that the special sciences all deal not with reality, but with systems of useful constructions of the mind, and that it is, therefore, left to philosophy to deal with reality itself, by intuition (Bergson),

by dialectic reasoning (Münsterberg), or by faith and reason (Duhem).

3. Mediating between 1. and 2. is the view that philosophy has a distinct subject matter of its own, but that this subject matter is no other than the system of the special sciences; that is, that philosophy is itself a special science, viz., the science of the sciences. This science may be conceived in quite naturalistic fashion. . . . "Sciences, then, are as real things as facts themselves. . . . We can analyze them as we analyze facts, investigate their elements, composition, order, and subject" (Taine). However, the view which, owing to the influence of Herbart, Wundt, and the Neo-Kantians, has prevailed for the last generation, has been a more critical one. It is supposed to be the business of philosophy to analyze and criticize the fundamental concepts and assumptions of the special sciences, and to build up a *consistent* world view on the basis of this critical work.

In spite, however, of all these diverse views as to the nature of philosophy, all are substantially agreed that its aim is to give us a coherent view, or outline chart, of the universe and the place in it of man, the external world, and the higher reality, if there be any. There is also a practical agreement that a department of philosophy in a college or university should teach metaphysics (including philosophy of mind and philosophy of religion), logic, ethics, aesthetics, and the history of philosophy. The late Professor Fullerton made the interesting attempt to show that these apparently diverse disciplines (including psychology) have not been grouped together by mere accident, but that they all have something fundamental in common, viz., that they all raise problems of reflective thought, i.e., problems involving the critical examination of the meaning of our ideas.

The history of modern American philosophy may also be divided roughly into three periods, the theologic, the metaphysical, and the scientific. The first of these periods might be dated from the beginning of the *Journal of Speculative*

Philosophy, the second from the beginning of the *Philosophical Review,* and the third from the *Journal of Philosophy, Psychology, and Scientific Methods.* This division into periods probably does as much violence to the facts of the case as any other, but it has the merit of calling attention to a certain shifting of the center of gravity of philosophic discussion. During the dominance of the St. Louis School, the motive of philosophy was well reflected in the motto of the *Journal of Speculative Philosophy:* "Philosophy can bake no bread, but she can procure for us God, freedom, and immortality." The leaders of this movement were not academic or professional teachers of philosophy, but rather, like Brockmeyer and Dr. Harris, practical men who believed they had found, from their superior point of view, fruitful insight into the fields of religion, art, history, education, and even practical politics. With the founding of the *Philosophical Review,* the control of philosophy passed into the hands of a number of college professors, most of whom had been taught in Germany. This tended to make philosophy more secular, and the dominant conception of philosophy was the one which associated it most intimately with science. Philosophy was thus conceived as an architectonic science, criticizing the assumptions of the special sciences, and supplementing the latter by building up their results into a complete *Weltanschauung.* This view was held by most of the pupils of Wundt, and, in this country, perhaps most characteristically carried out by Professor Ladd. The greater intimacy, however, between philosophy and the special sciences during recent years has brought to light the following considerations: that the criticism of the assumptions of the various sciences can be made only by those who are already in possession of a certain definite *Weltanschauung;* that there are no contradictions infesting the special sciences to such an extent that the scientists are helpless and need the aid of philosophers; and that the fundamental concepts of the different sciences can be analyzed only in the light of the special content of these sciences, and that the specialist is, if he undertakes it, the best qualified to make this analysis. At any rate for our purpose, this second period may be said to have ended with the publication of Royce's *The World and the Individual* and Ward's *Naturalism and Agnosticism*.

Since the publication of Dewey's *Studies in Logical Theory*, philosophy seems to have entered on a new career, the distinctive aims of which are, on the one hand, to give up the old idea of philosophy as a critique of the special sciences, and, on the other hand, to make philosophic discussion itself scientific, i.e., to narrow it down to certain definite and decidable issues. Professor Woodbridge put the first of these aims to the foreground in his presidential address before the Western Philosophical Association in 1903 thus: "I modestly shrink from a calling that imposes upon me the necessity of completing the fragmentary work of the physicist, the chemist, and the biologist, or of instructing these men in the basal principles of their respective sciences. My work lies in a totally different sphere, deals with totally different problems, and can be pursued in independence of them as much as they pursue their work in independence of me." [1]

Professor Dewey emphasizes the second of the above-mentioned aims. He expressly breaks with the tradition that philosophy has to do with a certain mode of life or with such concepts as God, freedom, and immortality. In an article on the "Postulates of Immediate Empiricism," [2] he tells us bluntly that, considered as a species of sanctions, philosophic conceptions have outlived their usefulness and that the only road open is that of immediate empiricism, which we are assured is identical with that of science.

It is thus seen that while the movement under consideration tends to dissociate philosophy not only from ethics and theology, but also from the *content* of the special sciences, it really aims to erect philosophy into a modest special science, dealing with definite problems and giving definite answers, so

[1] *The Philosophical Review*, Vol. XII, pp. 370 f.
[2] *The Journal of Philosophy*, Vol. II, p. 399.

that he who runs in this busy land may read the authoritative answer.

In spite of all appearances to the contrary, Professor James's books are no exception to this general tendency. With all his intensely human sympathies, his conception of philosophy is really of this last type. To students of philosophy his volume on *Pragmatism* simply raised a highly technical issue: How is truth to be defined? Nor does the volume on a *Pluralistic Universe* center its attention on a genuinely new view of the universe. Accepting the current vague theism, Professor James devotes his energies to disproving one of the ways in which this theism is sometimes established, viz., the Royce-Bradleyan arguments for the absolute. To those who come to philosophy for the relief of a certain cosmic anguish, who are troubled by old-fashioned doubts about the meaning of life and destiny, who cannot see whether there is or is not a divine government of the world in which we find ourselves, Professor James does not seem to offer any new or direct answer.

If anyone is inclined to minimize the extent to which the historical and wider conception of philosophy has been superseded by this narrower conception, let him reflect on the fate of Professor Ormond's volume, *Concepts of Philosophy*. This important book, the result of a whole lifetime of reflection covering the whole field of philosophy, has scarcely caused a ripple on the philosophic waters, and to many of our younger philosophers it appeared simply as a survival from a past which philosophy has rightly outlived.

Now the effect of our current reduction of philosophy to a purely formal discipline, viz., epistemology, cannot be said to have as yet increased vital interest in philosophy. Pragmatism, it is true, has made a great stir in our popular magazines, but is it really the pragmatic theory, rather than Professor James's striking style? As for his younger apostles, many of us, I dare say, have found them more brilliant than illuminating. Certainly flashes of genius cannot permanently take the place of the steady light of reason. Professors Dewey's and Tufts' superb textbook on *Ethics* is simply a continuation of the anthropologic method so clearly applied in this field by Wundt and Höffding. In theology the antihistorical bias of pragmatists generally prevents them from joining forces with the only group of genuine pragmatic theologians, the Ritschlian—for the latter trace their descent from Kant, and this is anathema to the ordinary pragmatist.

Nor has the new realism been any more fruitful. It is only a confirmed idealist like Royce or Münsterberg that can still find his philosophy in such intimate contact with the content of life that he has to overstep the bounds of his particular academic function.

It may be noted in passing that while philosophers have thus been withdrawing from contact with science, scientists have not been afraid to lay their secular hands on the sacred ark of metaphysics—witness Russell among mathematicians, Ostwald among chemists, Driesch and his disciples among biologists. The significance of this latter movement for philosophy is a very important question which the limits of this paper prevent us from considering now—we only need to notice here the irrepressible nature of metaphysics. No sooner is it suppressed in one place than it suddenly springs up in most unexpected quarters.

It is also worthy of note that in spite of Professor Dewey's yielding of what he considers the debatable fields of philosophy, and his concentration on those problems which alone admit of a scientific solution, the result of his work has not certainly so far reduced the irreconcilable differences among philosophers, nor does it even seem to tend in that direction.

I shall attempt to question later whether this excessive modesty on the part of recent philosophy is a genuine virtue. So far I have only attempted to show that if a virtue at all, it has not been a very profitable one.

The cause of this last change in the conception of philosophy is to be sought in the conditions of university teaching, for nearly all of our philosophers are now professional teachers. The period between 1890 and 1900 was one of rapid expansion for the American colleges. The most important of them were then transformed into real universities. Now the conditions of university teaching require a far higher degree of specialization on the part of pupils and teachers than the old college did. The old college teacher—of whom the late Professor Garman was a striking example—had to teach the whole field of philosophy, and could not, therefore, avoid bringing his subject into intimate relation with the various branches of science and life. The university teacher of logic, psychology, metaphysics, or even of ethics, as a rule feels no responsibility for the student's total view of the universe. Few teachers in any department of a university have the time or courage to poach on another's preserves, and teachers of philosophy are especially timid about venturing into fields in which they are not specialists. Thus the old idea of philosophy as a kind of universal knowledge, so vigorously maintained by Paulsen, no longer finds any adherents.

Now if we assume the possibility or desirability of philosophy in the old sense, i.e., a working view of the universe and of man's place in it, it is of course indispensable for the philosopher to be acquainted with the results and something of the procedure of the special sciences. But is this task really as impossible as our excessively modest friends would have us believe? Are we prepared to accept the view that the work of the special sciences is of an esoteric nature which none but the initiated may comprehend? If they do have something to tell to the world at large, why may not the philosopher, if he takes the trouble, learn it as well as anyone else? With the rapid expansion of the different sciences this task may seem impossible, and it is certainly a difficult one. Moreover, it subjects the philosopher to the most perilous of all dangers, the danger of being considered a dilettante. But the wisdom of life seems to show that as much is lost by excessive timidity as by recklessness.

The great strength of the new movement lies in the serious

way in which it takes and applies the idea of philosophy as a science. Once we consistently adopt this ideal there is no doubt but that a good deal of what has always been regarded as philosophy must go overboard. But is it necessary to accept this ideal? So long as life is wider than knowledge, may not the task of the philosopher be different from that of the scientist? There are undoubtedly many fields of philosophy, like logic, which are capable of being developed into strict sciences, and any progress in that direction is undoubtedly a great gain, but to admit this is not to admit that the whole of philosophy can be reduced to logic or epistemology, or to any science at all.

The idea that philosophy may not be a science is so repugnant to professional philosophic teachers that it seems almost futile to maintain such a thesis. The reasons for such repugnancy, however, are extraneous rather than essential. The wonderful achievements of science during the past one hundred years have thrown a glamour over the word itself so that even philosophers are not free from the allurements thereof. Moreover, everyone who has to teach undergraduates is forced to emphasize the certainty and definiteness of philosophic doctrines as against the vague and arbitrary opinions of untrained minds. One fact, however, must always prove a veritable thorn in the side of those who believe philosophy to be a science—and that is the fact that in spite of 2,500 years of warfare, in spite of the fact that all methods have been tried—the mathematical by Spinoza, the experimental by Hume, and so on—there is still a complete absence of any consensus. There is no such thing as a definite philosophy which can be taught impersonally. There are still only philosophies of different schools, and the choice between them is largely a matter of vital or temperamental preference.

This absence of any consensus has, of course, been only too obvious to the rest of the world, and those who maintain the scientific character of philosophy have had a hard time trying to minimize or explain away the fundamental differences of the various schools. From time to time, however, some conscientious person suggests the other alternative, viz., the construction of a philosophic platform which will bring into clearness the fundamental agreements. Thus it is hoped to usher in the philosophic millennium, when the idealistic lamb shall lie down beside the realistic wolf, or perhaps when some pragmatic tiger shall so have swallowed up all opposition that complete peace shall reign thereafter—at any rate, the swords of controversy shall be changed into the plowshares of empirical investigation. But the believers in philosophy as a science seem peculiarly unresponsive to this appeal. Like other Utopian ideals, it does not seem to have the potency to bring warring schools together, and the reign of complete peace among philosophers seems as far off as the reign of complete justice on earth, which Renan confidently tells us is at least 100,000 years off.

No doubt there has always been controversy among scientists also, but those have been restricted to particular fields and have always been regarded as capable of being definitely decided one way or another—witness the heliocentric theory, natural selection, etc. Can philosophy show any such results? An attempt to formulate propositions to which all philosophers could subscribe would be devoid of genuine philosophic significance, for these propositions would have different connotations in the different schools.

A number of years ago Dr. Kate Gordon, in an article entitled "Metaphysics as a Branch of Art," propounded the interesting thesis that art and metaphysics deal with general ideas, while science deals with particular facts—that the truths of art and of metaphysics are felt truths, but are not facts which have at any time been demonstrated. In a subsequent controversy with Dr. Ewer, her challenge that he point out some respect in which metaphysics and science agree, remained unanswered. Now it is easy enough to deny her thesis by showing the inadequacy of her antithesis between particular facts and general ideas. Well-developed sciences deal with general laws rather than with particular facts; and mathematics is as much a study of the implications of certain general ideas as a study of particular facts. It is likewise easy to show that the fundamental motive for metaphysics is the same as that of pure science generally, viz., *the desire to know the truth*.[3] Philosophy and science both agree in their desire to eliminate arbitrary opinion, in their insistence on method or system and on logical rigor or consistency, and in their effort to eliminate external authority, prejudice, personal interest and the like, in the consideration of what is true.

At the same time a careful consideration of its history shows that, unlike science, philosophy has never been able entirely to dispense with pure speculation, nor has it been able entirely to eliminate the bias of temperament, and in these respects philosophy resembles a certain art, viz., the art of poetry and of reflective literature generally. Actual scientific knowledge is too fragmentary to enable us to form a complete picture of the world to which we must react, and so imagination must be called in. Sometimes imagination and science work together, but often imagination does all the work and science is a silent spectator, as in the case of Fechner's *Zend-Avesta*.

It has generally been assumed that of two opposing systems of philosophy, e.g., realism and idealism, one only *can* be true and one *must* be false; and so philosophers have been hopelessly divided on the question, which is the true one. The assumption back of this attitude is that philosophy is determinate knowledge which will not admit of variation. But is this assumption necessary? Cannot two pictures of the same

[3] This last assertion may by many be regarded as a blatant platitude, but it is really an important truth which needs to be vigorously defended against those who would subordinate pure science to its practical applications, and metaphysics to theological and ethical considerations. Whatever its origin, the passion for knowledge is with many natures as profound as the desire for material comfort, and the satisfaction of this passion as important as the invention of gasoline engines and other philosophically doubtful blessings.

object both be true, in spite of radical differences? The picture which the philosopher draws of the world is surely not one in which every stroke is necessitated by pure logic. A creative element is surely present in all great systems, and it does not seem possible that all sympathy or fundamental attitudes of will can be entirely eliminated from any human philosophy. The method of exposition which philosophers have adopted leads many to suppose that they are simply inquirers, that they have no interest in the conclusions at which they arrive, and that their primary concern is to follow their premises to their logical conclusions. But it is not impossible to think that the minds of philosophers sometimes act like those of other mortals, and that, having once been determined by diverse circumstances to adopt certain views, they then look for and naturally find reasons to justify these views.

There are a number of points in which the method of philosophers is precisely that of literary essayists of the type of Sainte-Beuve, Matthew Arnold, Stevenson, or Lowell. Both use examples to suggest or illustrate rather than to demonstrate. In science this would be called the fallacy of one example. In both literature and philosophy the temper of the lesser Napoleon, *aut Caesar aut nullus,* is very prominent. In science this might be called the "all or nothing" fallacy. Constant reservations and numerous qualifications destroy literary sweep, and take away the air of profundity from philosophic discussion. Some philosophers, notably Aristotle and St. Thomas Aquinas, might perhaps be excepted from the last statement, but in spite of all our hankering after the epithet science, I cannot see that we have been making much progress in this habit of self-control against the extravagance of generalization. Again, both literature and philosophy work by appealing to certain reigning idols. These idols come into vogue in different ways. They are seldom refuted or directly overthrown. Generally they are simply outlived, or they do not survive the change of fashion. In the later eighties or in the earlier nineties the term *relation* was a magic word to

conjure with. It was brought into mode by Thomas Hill
Green, and died a natural death with the eclipse of his influence. Today if anything is characterized as *experimental,
functional,* or *dynamic,* that is enough to allow it to pass all
the watch dogs of philosophic criticism, and to characterize
anything as *static* is to consign it to the lowermost depths from
which no power can rescue it. I am not anxious to bring down
the wrath of the gods by questioning the all-sufficient potency
of such terms as *experience* and *evolution;* but may I ask what
progress would mathematical physics have made if every
time one approached a problem of stresses, he were frightened
off by the warning that he must not for a moment entertain
that most heinous criminal, the static point of view? I humbly
agree with those who claim that the static point of view is
mechanical and lifeless and, therefore, inapplicable to the
entire universe, but I am quite sure that the dynamic point of
view itself may be mechanical and lifeless.

Lastly, literature and philosophy both allow past idols to
be resurrected with a frequency which would be truly distressing to a sober scientist. If a philosophic theory is once ruled
out of court, no one can tell when it will appear again. There
is no doctrine of *res adjudicata,* or statute of limitations in
metaphysics. Those of us who have been taught to read the
Greek philosophers with a degree of care have always supposed that Plato had once for all and forever refuted the
Protagorean doctrine of absolute relativism, but Mr. Schiller
with characteristic English conservatism has urged us to move
the hands of the philosophic clock back a trifle of over 2,300
years.

In thus pointing out certain respects in which philosophy
resembles literature more than science, I do not mean, of
course, to imply that it would be well for philosophy if it
ceased to aim at scientific rigor. Let philosophy resolutely aim
to be as scientific as possible, but let her not forget her strong
kinship with literature.

Has philosophy more affinity for chemistry than for political science? or are the methods of the philosopher more like those of the cytologist than of the sociologist? Tradition would have us believe that the natural sciences are exact, that the social sciences are inexact, and that philosophy resembles the first group. But this is questionable from all its three ends.

A philosophy which would recognize its kinship with literature and with the social sciences would be truly humanistic. It would aim to be scientific, but it would not be afraid to go beyond science, just as life and conduct must go beyond knowledge. This, however, would be only a reassertion of the old ideal of philosophy as mediating between the *Lebensanschauung* of literature and the social sciences, and the *Weltanschauung* of the natural sciences. We may laugh at system building as much as we please, but some such ideal must be held up by somebody if the present anarchic tendency to overspecialization is to be controlled in the interests of sanity. If not, we shall soon have a condition in which everyone is a specialist and no one can intelligently follow his neighbor— a condition to which meetings of our mathematical societies are rapidly approximating.

This ideal of philosophy is also one which gives special significance to the teaching of it in our American colleges. It is in harmony with the recent reassertion of the old ideal of culture as the aim of college training, so vigorously put forth by both President Lowell and President Hadley. If the elective system is to be continued in any way, and if the college is to train men rather than entomologists or geometers, we need some integrating study that shall keep apace with and balance the progress of specialization. We have been too much afraid of the bugbear of dilettantism. Even in science half a loaf is better than nothing at all, especially if the whole loaf is unattainable even to the specialist himself.

PHILOSOPHY AND
SCIENTIFIC METHODS

I

IT MAY SEEM presumptuous for one who is not himself a scientist to lecture to you on the scientific method. But I propose only to raise questions for discussion rather than to instruct you. In doing so I shall proceed on the dictum of the famous American philosopher, Josh Billings, that "It is better not to know so much than to know so much that ain't so."

It sounds rather paradoxical to assert that with regard to the nature of the scientific method scientists themselves are not always possessed of clear and sound ideas. Yet on reflection this ought not to seem incredible. Men who have attained old age in good health are not necessarily competent to tell others how to achieve it. Nor is the successful businessman always instructive when he comes back to college and very naïvely explains to the young hopefuls how he achieved his success, generally attributing it to some platitude that he learned from his Greek professor, or from somebody else who didn't know anything about his business. Now men working in a laboratory generally follow certain techniques that are established habits or routines in their field, so that the trained worker cannot readily depart from them, and he thus becomes almost incapable of making certain kinds of mistakes. But when he begins to generalize about the scientific method as such, he is apt to, and generally does, repeat the conventional (and I venture to think erroneous) views of a lawyer named Bacon, or of a public administrator such as J. S. Mill.

The proof of the fact that men of great scientific achievement do not always clearly grasp the essence of the scientific method outside of their own field of research is shown by the character of their utterances on politics, religion, and all sorts of other issues. To avoid invidious personal references, let me cite a round robin signed a few years ago by a number of leaders of American science, in co-operation with a number of liberal Protestant theologians and a number of businessmen. It contained a declaration that according to the teaching of science, "God reveals himself through countless ages in the development of the earth as an abode for men, and in the agelong inbreathing of life into its constituent matter." Now, no one questions the right of anyone engaged in some branch of science to express the theologic beliefs that he shares with the fellow members of his religious denomination. But to assert that these beliefs are founded on science is to ignore completely the nature of scientific evidence, the determination of which is the essence of the scientific method. If the statement in question were true, there could not be any atheists or agnostics among scientific geologists and biologists. Now one need not refer to the actual inquiry of Professor Leuba, which shows that atheists and agnostics are more frequent among men of science than among the rest of the population. Nor need one even mention such outstanding figures as Huxley and Jacques Loeb. It is sufficient to point to the general recognition by religious as well as nonreligious thinkers, that the methods of proof in empirical sciences like geology and biology are not suitable to establish any proposition about God's plans, or even whether life was or was not breathed into matter.

Nothing, it seems, could be plainer than the distinction between the truths of science, which are verifiable by anyone who repeats the experiments or calculation, and the personal opinions of men of science about questions outside the field of their special competence. Why then is the distinction so often ignored, not only by the public and the press but also by distinguished men of science? I venture to suggest that in the public mind the scientist has taken the place formerly held by the priest, as one having access to absolute truth or omniscience. Very few can follow accurate reports of scientific work, and so most people accept popularized and oversimplified accounts of it on faith. Nowadays men working in some particular branch of science are necessarily laymen in other fields, for no one today can cover all the various fields or even keep up with reliable reports as to what is being achieved in them.

It might be supposed that the scientific habit, of drawing no conclusion except on the basis of rigorous and accurate evidence, could be carried over from the domain of one's training into any other region. But actual instances show that this is not always the case in regard to social, political, and religious issues. The discreet silence that it would generally involve goes against the human grain. How can we be silent when everyone about us is confidently certain?

II

If we distinguish as we must between the verifiable truths of science and the fallible opinions of the individual scientist, we may define science as a self-corrective system. A system of theology, for instance, cannot admit that it may be mistaken in any part. Its truths once revealed must remain indubitable. If you doubt you get out of the system and are lost in outer darkness. But *science invites doubt*. It can grow or make progress, not only because it is fragmentary, but also because no one proposition in it is in itself absolutely certain, and so the process of correction can operate when we find more adequate evidence. But note, however, that the doubt and the correction are always in accordance with the canons of the scientific method, so that the latter is the bond of continuity.

One might draw a parallel in this respect between science and constitutional government. A constitutional government is one in which every particular law or institution can be corrected or abolished by constitutional means. This is not possible in an absolute monarchy, or in any form of dictatorship.

In the latter you either accept the whole or else have to over-throw it all. Science may thus be viewed as the method by which any particular proposition, which we now believe to be true, may be corrected on the basis of new evidence. Consider, for instance, the great *Syntaxis* of Ptolemy. Contrary to a popular impression today among those who do not read him, Ptolemy was a great scientist. He had the real essence of the scientific method in him. His observations and those of others were carefully correlated. His reasoning was closely articulated, and his book is still a good example of a scientific treatise. But he proceeded on a hypothesis that has been replaced by a simpler one, since Copernicus reduced the number of epicycles. Moreover, the Copernican astronomy now fits in with a type of physics that enables us to discover a mechanism for the motion of the stars and to show that this mechanism is precisely the same as the mechanism of earthly motion. The new hypothesis thus enables us to enlarge and correct our previous knowledge, but it does not prove that the old one is all wrong. Newton sometimes relied on Ptolemy. If every new discovery simply replaced all previous knowledge, we should have something like an oriental dynastic change where the new regime kills off all the remnants of the old regime which it displaces. The progress of science is not a complete replacing of the old by the new, but a process of continual self-correction.

If we approach the problem of the scientific method from this point of view, we can, I think, prevent some misunderstandings that hinder clear analysis.

III

SOME of the misunderstandings of the nature of science arise from the fact that today scientists are not generally trained in history, i.e., in the interpretation of ancient documents or records. The terminology of modern science has changed so rapidly that it is impossible today for a physicist or an astronomer, unless he is a careful historical scholar, to read the Latin writings of the Renaissance or Middle Ages and really get their modern equivalent. Even those physicists who have some knowledge of Latin find Newton's *Principia* difficult reading, because his terminology as well as his synthetic method is no longer familiar. On the other hand, professional historians generally do not know much about the history of science because they are not familiar with the subject matter. Thus you have the recent spectacle of a presumably great historian who says in effect that there was practically no science before the seventeenth century; that before that time there was a lot of speculation but no observation of facts; that the idea that we ought to build up science from the observation of facts never occurred to anybody before the time of Bacon, Galileo, and Descartes. All mankind was blind and lived in utter scientific darkness, according to this account, until these three men, about the same time, conceived the brilliant idea that instead of speculating they would observe the facts, and so they gave birth to science. Now that, I think, represents a prevalent myth about the history of science. And it is one of the many myths that the future will record as current in this age which thinks of itself as scientific, but is as full of its own superstition and mythology as any other age.

It is not difficult to recognize the existence of science before the seventeenth century. All we have to do is to look at the works of men such as Euclid, Archimedes, Ptolemy, or Hippocrates. There is not in fact a single one of the sciences of which the foundations were not laid in Grecian times. Whether you take mathematics, astronomy, mechanics, hydrostatics, optics, physiology, zoology, or botany, or any other science, you will find that the elements were clearly expounded before the third century A.D.

My theme is not the history of science. But I do wish to call attention to a myth about the scientific method, namely, that it consists in banishing all hypotheses or anticipations of nature and begins with the observation of the facts themselves. Francis Bacon is the hero of this myth. Bacon was not only a courtier but a lawyer trained in the professional Inns of Court. So he conceived the idea that nature could be studied in just the way that law was studied in his day, that is, *by cases.* According to this view, if you went out into the field and recorded the facts of nature, according to schedules outlined in the *Novum Organum,* you could build up all the sciences. (Bacon thought he could have done it himself if he were not so busy with other things.) This notion, which is dignified by the name of induction, has become so fashionable that nothing is so familiar in the intellectual world as the boast that one's procedure is inductive and not deductive.

Now that is a superstition for which, it seems to me, there is no justification except the initial disinclination to think. Reflection shows it to be absurd to suppose that the scientist begins with an empty mind, with a *tabula rasa,* on which he writes his observation of the facts. It would be interesting if those who talk this way about induction and the experimental method actually tried it. In point of fact we do not know what to look for unless we have some idea to start with. Actually the people who have made discoveries in any of the sciences have not followed the Baconian prescription of avoiding anticipations of nature. On the contrary, they have always been men who were not only familiar with what was already known in their field, but gifted with many anticipatory ideas which they tried to test. It is when a man of genius hits upon a fruitful idea that great discoveries become possible.

IV

IN THIS CONNECTION, it is well to be cautious about fashionable doctrines concerning the advantages of the open mind. It is true that too obstinate an attachment to an accepted theory may be a hindrance to progress,[1] but it ought also to be obvious that in science as elsewhere, no great achievements are possible without courage. And the persistence in a theory, though the facts seem at face value to be contrary, is one of the ways by which men like Copernicus and Einstein have secured great triumphs. To suppose that the sun does not move around the earth, or that relativity might be applied to gravitation and accelerated motion, seemed at first to fly in the face of the facts. But the scientist must be skeptical as to what are the facts. All too frequently they turn out to be accepted prejudices. One might, therefore, define science as the method whereby we ascertain what are the facts. When we know that, we don't need anything else.

In support of the empirical myth in the conventional history of science are the assertions that Kepler discovered the laws of planetary motion by looking at Tycho Brahe's tables, and that Galileo discovered the laws of falling bodies by rolling balls down inclined planes. I venture to assert that one who does not already have the geometry of conics in mind cannot possibly see Kepler's laws in Tycho Brahe's, or any other, astronomical table. In fact, we know that Kepler tried other theories before he tested whether the recorded observations would fit into the theory of ellipses. Similarly, I have no hesitation in maintaining that no one who tries Galileo's experiment on falling bodies, under the conditions that he tried it (without any machinery or even a highly accurate clock), will see his laws rigorously verified. We know that in fact he arrived at the idea of a simple proportionality between the elapsed time and the velocity acquired in it by a process of *a priori* reasoning (part of which was fallacious), and that he then made his experiments to test it and was satisfied with the rough results, because of his prior conviction that reality or the book of nature was conceived by the Creator in simple mathematical relations.

[1] See section IX.

Along with this it is interesting to note the persistence of the myth that Galileo disproved the Aristotelian theory that heavier bodies fall more rapidly, not by reasoning but by going to the leaning Tower of Pisa and dropping down two objects of unequal weight. Professor Lane Cooper has recently aroused the wrath of the scientific public by questioning the historicity of the incident.[2] But so far as I know, no one has yet brought forth adequate evidence to eliminate the doubt thus raised by Professor Cooper.

I must, however, pass over this and raise the more logical question: Suppose that Galileo had actually performed the experiment, what would it have proved? Popular philosophers who praise Galileo for resorting to observation and experiment seldom think of repeating the experiment, and it never occurs to them to remark that feathers, snowflakes, rain drops, hail, and pebbles do not all come down with the same speed. The most obvious fact is that the resistance of the air, as of any other medium, is not the same for all bodies. It is a commonplace of physical science that only in a vacuum would bodies of unequal weight come down with the same velocity, and that the retardation due to the friction of any medium, such as the air, does depend on the mass as well as on the shape of the falling bodies. Now, Aristotle (who did not believe in the existence of a vacuum) was doubtless wrong when he thought that in the air the velocities of falling bodies would be simply proportional to the masses. The functional relation is more complex than that. But Aristotle's error in this respect was generally recognized in antiquity (for instance by his commentator Philopoemen); and Lucretius gave a true and simple statement of what does happen.[3]

It is sad to find the issue inaccurately represented in such a wonderfully good book as Einstein and Infeld's *Evolution of Physics*. Myths all too frequently triumph over science.

[2] Lane Cooper, *Aristotle, Galileo, and the Tower of Pisa*. Cornell University Press, 1935.

[3] *Ibid.*, pp. 49 and 58 (a convenient source of Lucretius' statement).

V

BUT LET us come closer to our main theme—the nature of the scientific method. And here I am glad to avail myself of a very wise remark by Einstein: "If you want to know the essence of scientific method don't listen to what a scientist may tell you. Watch what he does." And I suppose we should qualify it, "Watch what he does when engaged in scientific work, not when he is taking a holiday or is on a picnic, or discoursing on something beyond his competence." If we take the advice and really follow the actual workings of scientific research, we find that one of its first conditions is a willingness to hold all our information as tentative or provisional. That means a willingness not to question all things at once, for that is impossible, but to question any one proposition by asking, "Is it so?" Of course, to most people that is generally an impossibility, because so many things seem to us too obvious to be questioned. But it also seems obvious that the earth is flat, and that the sun and stars revolve around us. Generally we do not hesitate to condemn anyone as mentally deficient, who does not see what we do. When no issue of great importance to us is involved, we let the poor fellow alone. But if he annoys us we may put him in a lunatic asylum or in prison, or perhaps kill him. But the questioning of the obvious is an essential service in science. And this is true both in regard to principles and what appear as facts.

All human disciplines, so far as they have aimed to be scientific, have not only used mathematics, but have till recently looked up to Euclidean geometry as a model of a scientific system. We can trace that influence even in politics, e.g., in the Declaration of Independence, with its appeal to certain truths as self-evident.

Euclidean geometry begins with certain axioms from which

certain propositions are deduced or demonstrated. And what does strict demonstration mean? It means that we can show it to be impossible to accept Euclid's axioms and not accept his theorems. But for over twenty centuries it never occurred to people to question the axiom that from a point outside of a straight line only one parallel can be drawn. In the nineteenth century, however, a Hungarian, Bolyai, and a Russian, Lobachevski, and subsequently a German, Riemann, by questioning that very self-evident proposition, opened up new fields in geometry. After the parallel axiom, others began to be doubted, for instance, that the part can never be equal to the whole. Startling as the last seems, it is yet true that the whole theory of transfinites is based on it. In a similar way the axioms of Newtonian mechanics are being questioned today, and a new physics is being developed in which we no longer accept the Newtonian conception of time and space as absolute, nor the absolute constancy of mass, nor the constant ratio between force and the acceleration of a body. Notice that Newton has not been thrown to the garbage heap as some popular accounts would have us believe: Newtonian physics is still sound, still true, but not sufficiently accurate for certain purposes. What we have achieved by our questioning is to correct Newton's generalizations by showing that they are only special applications of wider laws under limited conditions.

VI

Now, if you follow me, you can see that the same skeptical attitude must be observed in regard to what seem to be obvious and self-evident facts. In scientific work we must always be prepared to raise the question with regard to any assumed fact—is it so? One of the distinctions between science and common sense is precisely the fact that in science we are not satisfied merely to observe things and believe all we see. We must doubt, examine, and verify. To do this we must invent all sorts of apparatus and means to avoid seeing what doesn't exist and find ways and means of seeing what to the ordinary man is not usually visible. That most people see things or events that do not exist or happen is shown every day in courts of law. Witnesses often swear in good faith that they saw certain things, and when they are cross-examined it is proved conclusively that they were situated at certain points where what they think they saw was not at all visible. We all tend to see what we expect to see and science must help us to overcome that tendency. But science also invents instruments, like the telescope, microscope, and others, to enable us to see things that are not visible to the ordinary eye. In both of those ways, then, science enables us to answer more critically the question, is it so?

The foregoing, however, is not sufficient. One of the main causes that make common sense so unreliable and render our political discussion and our so-called social science so full of interminable controversies, is the failure to formulate our questions in definite terms.

Is man good or bad? Are you a pessimist or an optimist? Do you or do you not believe in the possession of private property; in the rights of man? All who answer these and similar questions in the affirmative or negative are agreed to despise those who refuse to answer before determining what precisely these terms mean.

If our procedure is to be scientific, our terms must be definite. And real definition of terms doesn't mean merely finding verbal equivalents. The clearest way of making our terms definite is by the process known as measurement.

What does measurement really accomplish? The answer is that it enables us to avoid such expressions as "this plant is big" (or small). Measurement gives us a number, which is definite; and the number enables us to correlate the length or weight of any particular object with any other object of the same kind. In that way we avoid all the vagueness of common categories, and by substituting definite terms we make issues clear and definite. When we do that, we can generalize and correlate various relations, and so have a system, enabling us to see things not in their isolation, but in their functioning or interaction with other objects.

VII

IF WE BEAR in mind the necessity of both actual observation and the correlation of our observations or measurements into a system, we can avoid all the fruitless controversies between induction and deduction. For it is not true that we can begin with pure facts any more than with pure theory, independent of facts. We always operate with both, and it is doubtful whether in adult intellectual life we ever find one of these factors alone. There is no scientific problem or research except where one asks how certain known facts are to be explained or their fuller nature discovered, e.g., what causes the heart to beat, or cancer to grow in certain tissues. And this means that we not only have our ideal of what would constitute a satisfactory explanation or completion of our knowledge, but also some anticipation (true or false) of the direction of the inquiry or research that will lead us to the desired result.

Doubtless, as was admitted before, obstinate clinging to old ideas hinders the discovery of new truth. But it is well to remember what the great naturalist Charles Darwin said on this point, that the mischief of false theories is slight compared with the mischief of false observations. For a false theory such as that of the phlogiston or the older views of nerve functions still enabled us to correlate a number of facts and thus reveal the need for some corrections, whereas *everything* built on a false observation has to be eliminated before progress can be resumed. Moreover, it is neither possible nor desirable to clear our minds of all anticipatory ideas or hypotheses. The facts of nature would not of themselves stream in properly ticketed and labeled into such emptied minds.

The real cure for obstinate bias is to multiply the number of possible hypotheses or points of view before us, just as the cure for fanaticism is to become familiar with other forms of belief. This is aided by formal logic which enables us to make our assumptions explicit and then to formulate their contraries or alternatives. This procedure is beautifully exemplified in Lobachevski's *Imaginary Geometry*.

It is only when we approach a problem with a number of alternative hypotheses in mind that the process of verification has any sense.

VIII

THE TERM "verification" has, indeed, become a kind of fetish to be worshiped, but not critically examined. Very few have actually analyzed its precise meaning. Now it seems to me that *verification* should be clearly distinguished from *confirmation*. Any hypothesis which explains things is to that extent confirmed. But every superstition can be confirmed in that way. If, for instance, you believe that thunder is caused by Zeus shaking his rod, every instance of thunder can confirm it. If you believe that everything a man does is due to his subconscious or unconscious ego, then everything that happens can be interpreted that way. But such confirmation is not verification for it does not exclude the possibility that some other theory may explain it just as well or even better.

Let me give you a concrete example of what I have in mind. A woman goes to a psychoanalyst and in talking freely she refers to a friend of hers by her maiden name. The psychoanalyst pounces on that and says, "You don't like her husband?" and she admits that she doesn't.

Freud uses this to prove that our dislikes prevent us from remembering certain things. Well, that is an explanation of the fact, if it is a fact. But some other explanation might be just as good or even better. For instance, on January 1st, January 2d, and some days thereafter, most of us keep on writing the old year. Is that due to the fact that we don't like the new year or have some sort of prejudice against it? The explanation in terms of habit seems better because it explains so many other things without more arbitrary assumptions. Scientific verification consists not in accepting a hypothesis because it explains things, but in comparing two different hypotheses and seeing which explanation is better.

Now consider this question of memory: Why do we remember some things and not others? Formerly we used to talk about the faculty of memory, but that did not provide any basis for the distinction. Now the advantage of the hypothesis that memory is physiologically conditioned is that it enables us to deduce possible experiments as to what kind of physical things or sounds are more easily remembered than others, and the results of such experiments either confirm or refute our hypothesis. Confirmation, therefore, is not itself a distinctive trait of science, because every belief can be confirmed if we wish to hold on to it.

If you are a pious Mohammedan and believe that everything happens according to the will of Allah, then every event will confirm that faith. But by the same procedure non-Mohammedan faiths can also be confirmed. The difference between verification and confirmation, then, consists in the fact that the former involves some differential or critical test.

This is clearly illustrated by the experiments of Fresnel and Young on the diffraction of light. If the Newtonian corpuscular theory were true, certain results should follow, contrary to what would be the case if Huyghens' theory of waves were true, and vice versa. And so an experiment that confirms one but contradicts the other shows the first to be preferable. The actual results of the experiment were contrary to what followed on the corpuscular, but agreed with what was to be expected on the wave, theory. This made the wave theory the preferable one. The same is true in regard to the difference between the continental theory of Ampère that electricity acts at a distance, and the English theory of Faraday that electricity acts through a medium. No preferences between the two theories could be scientifically established until we had a crucial experiment. This was the discovery of Hertzian waves —which can be reconciled with the Faraday theory, but not with the continental theory. It is only when of two theories, one explains the facts that are in conflict with the other, that we have real verification. What verification does, then, is not to prove a theory, but to show that of those available, one is the most probable.

It is well, however, to keep in mind that one experiment or observation may be inadequate. Thus for years the believers in the Ptolemaic astronomy urged that the Copernican hypothesis could not be true because if it were true, Venus, being an inner planet between the sun and the earth, should show certain phases like the moon. But since it didn't, the Copernican astronomy was held to be demonstrably false. This was in fact a sound argument against the Copernican astronomy, but was shown to be baseless when people began to use the telescope and the phases of Venus became actually visible.

It seems to me that if we take the foregoing view of verification, we can make some sense out of Mill's canons. Consider Mill's formulation of the method of agreement and the method of difference. The first asserts in effect that if you observe instances of any phenomenon all you have to do is to note what is a common circumstance and you have the cause. Now suppose you want to know the cause of cancer. Obviously there are all sorts of common circumstances that are not the cause of cancer. It is only some differential circumstance, that is to say, some circumstance that is present whenever cancer is present and absent whenever cancer is not present, that can be a cause; and so we are driven to the method of difference. But even that might not be sufficient. Things may be accidentally correlated for a long time and yet not be causally connected. To establish a causal connection there must be an intimate relation; there must be some relation of identity of substance or energy, and Mill's canons give us no clue as to how to find it.

Consider, however, an actual situation when we are approaching a problem with a number of possible alternative hypotheses as to what, e.g., might be the cause of cancer. Then Mill's canons formulate with some degree of appropriateness how by the process of verification I eliminate circumstances that fail to meet the requisites of a cause, i.e., of being necessary and sufficient conditions for the phenomenon observed.

IX

MOST PEOPLE draw a sharp distinction between natural science and social science. There is some justification for this, but it is unfortunately misleading as a dichotomy. If there are facts about human nature they are just as much the object of natural science as any other facts. The real difficulty, however, is that students of social science are interested not only in facts of existence, but in promoting certain more or less partisan purposes. Thus whenever we deal with sociology, or politics, or economics, or any of the so-called applied sciences, we are concerned with two different kinds of questions: (1) how things exist and are connected, and (2) how to promote certain purposes.

The problem of human purpose is a difficult one because it does not seem that all human beings do have in fact the same purposes. And if there actually are ultimate differences of purpose, it may not be possible to come to any agreement. In other words, when people really want different things you cannot prove that they don't want what they do want.

Mr. Bertrand Russell has said with regard to philosophers that the reason they do not attain truth is because they do not want to, meaning that they prefer to maintain their points of view rather than see the truth. Well, whether that is true or not about philosophers, it is certainly true in social studies.

For in the latter field we are much more anxious to achieve certain results, and our minds are thus closed to the possibility that we may be wrong in our fundamental assumptions.

Take a concrete example: There are in the world today at least three different theories concerning what is the best form of government. Now, all of those theories are being tried experimentally in the different countries. Which works best? There seems to be great difficulty in deciding that objectively. Partisans of each one of these theories point to the country in which the experiment is being tried and say: "There, you see how well it works!" Well, the others are not willing to accept their judgment as to whether communism does work well in Russia, whether fascism works well in Germany or Italy, or whether democracy works well in our own country. These questions cannot be settled so far as I can see by the same canons by which we settle questions of physics. Moreover, the problems of social science are much more complicated because they involve not only the elements of physics and biology, but additional historical and psychologic consideration. And at that we still have many unsolved problems in physics, e.g., the problem of what will happen if you take an ordinary chair and spin it around: the mathematical equations are exceedingly complex.

It is by no means certain that our methods will keep on growing until we do solve all of our difficulties. It does not even seem highly probable that we shall ever reduce all social phenomena to relations so simple that they can be easily dealt with by a manageable system of equations. Nevertheless, the hope is there and the history of science indicates that many things that seemed unsolvable, sooner or later yielded to the human resolution to solve them. This gives us no assurance, but makes hope possible.

X

PROCEEDINGS OF THE SEMINAR

Dr. Blaisdell: Professor Cohen, speaking for myself, I enjoyed your lecture very much last night, and I suppose it is because you said some things that I agree with. If some of the rest of the people here feel differently, perhaps it will be because they disagree with some of the things you said, and that ought to be a good situation for starting the discussion.

Dr. Schwartz: Considering the many important discoveries in science that have been made by accident rather than by design, and that the biological sciences in particular have used the method of direct observation with and without instruments of precision; that many of the fundamental discoveries in biology have resulted from observation, and sometimes by persons without training in science: must we not say, therefore, that the method of biological science is largely inductive rather than deductive?

Dr. Cohen: Well, if I assumed your facts, I suppose I should draw the same conclusion, but I should not grant your assumptions to be facts. In the first place, I should not admit that any great discovery in science has been made by accident. I know that conventional history books say so; but every account that I have checked up has proved to be erroneous. Let me give you some classic cases. It is said that Roentgen discovered X-rays (or Roentgen rays) by accident—just picked up a photographic plate, and finding a picture of a key, naturally concluded that a new kind of radiation must have caused it. But, in point of fact, Roentgen had previously devoted years of study to the different kinds of radiations, so that the accident was the kind that could happen only to one who had thought as much about the subject as he had. *It is only because he was ready to see the importance of that particular picture* that he discovered the rays that caused it.

Some books also say that it was by accident that Hertz discovered electric waves. But if you read what Hertz himself says you learn that he was for years concerned with the question of whether the existence of electric waves could be shown. He had been set that problem by Helmholtz to test Faraday's theory of the ether. Otherwise he would not have recognized what he saw as electric waves. Nor do I know of a single important discovery made in scientific biology by anyone to whom it was not a matter of special interest and study. Of course, you can mention early observers like Leeuwenhoek, who was only a janitor. But I think we must get rid of the notion that a man's intellectual equipment is determined by his social position or office. Leeuwenhoek was, undoubtedly, a keenly interested and close observer, because he was looking for definite things. The ordinary man can look through a microscope but he doesn't see anything of importance. I know, for I looked through microscopes when I was a student, and could not see anything except patches of what looked like mud. I was told to draw what I saw, but I couldn't draw anything definite when I saw nothing definite. Some ideas are required before you can have really intelligent observation. We see with our mind's eye as well as with our physical eye: and seeing with our mind's eye is precisely what is meant by having anticipatory ideas.

DR. TUCKERMAN: I am wondering whether that is quite clear. I am puzzled about your viewpoint. Take Leeuwenhoek, for instance. He saw things and then he saw more things, and after a while, he said, "What does that mean?" I have just been reading Dobell's book *Antony van Leeuwenhoek and His Little Animals* (Harcourt, Brace, 1932). I could find no preconceived ideas in the excerpts from Leeuwenhoek's writings. The generalizations he made were built out of the things he saw after he had seen them. He was interested, yes, he had a mind, yes; but did he first have a lot of preconceived notions that he tried to verify?

DR. COHEN: Most decidedly, yes. My point is this: unless he had anticipatory ideas, he would not have noticed the things that he saw. Take people from the street, give them a microscope with the sort of things Leeuwenhoek had before him, and ask them what they see. Try it.

DR. TUCKERMAN: I tried it myself as a kid when I got a microscope, and I saw things I never heard of.

DR. COHEN: If you had seen what Leeuwenhoek saw you would be in his class.

MR. WILCOX: I should like to ask how your theory differs from the more usual type of explanation of the scientific method. To make it concrete, would you indicate the steps in your outline in contrast with the four steps in the classic illustration of the discovery of Neptune, taking as the conventional outline: (1) *Observations* of the positions of the planets by Tycho Brahe, (2) *Induction* into the three laws of Kepler; further induction into one law by Newton, (3) *Deduction,* in the form of mathematical computations by Leverrier and Adams, leading to the theoretical position of an unknown planet whose existence was set up as a hypothesis to account for the irregularities in the orbit of the outermost known planet, (4) *Verification,* when Galle set his telescope in the indicated position and discovered Neptune (September 1846). The point I am asking is how does your explanation of the scientific method differ from those classic four steps?

DR. COHEN: It differs because I do not believe that mere observation is the first step. For, as pointed out before, in order that the observation should be significant, in order to find anything of importance in science, we have to know what to look for. Take the example given in some books—the example that you gave—namely, Kepler looking at Tycho Brahe's tables and seeing the planetary laws. That is a most absurd story and no one who has ever seen those tables or read any of Kepler's works can for a moment believe it. The fact that the thing is current in textbooks shows to what depth of ignorance reputable writers on logic and the history of science can descend. If ellipses were so obvious in looking at Tycho Brahe's tables, why did not Tycho Brahe himself see them? Why did he invent his compromise between Ptolemy and Copernicus? In fact the figures of Tycho Brahe's tables do not fit into ellipses with perfect accuracy. Kepler himself tells us of his various other attempts to explain the planetary motions before he hit upon the theory of ellipses. Assuming with Galileo that the planetary motions must conform to some Greek geometric pattern he tried the theory that the paths of the planets would be found in the circumscribed spheres of the five regular solids. If you read the introduction to his treatise on Mars, you will see he did not begin with the theory of ellipses, and that it was suggested to him by Apollonius of Perga's treatise on conic sections after other theories failed to fit the observations.

MR. BEAN: You mean in a simple case, where we have two columns of figures, it would be possible to see a curve in those two columns?

DR. COHEN: I should say no one curve is definitely determined by any column of observations. What we actually do is precisely what Kepler did in essence. We try a number of theoretical curves and see which fits best with the actual readings. Anyone who has ever done any curve fitting knows that if you take any column of figures and try to fit a curve to them, you have to do a lot of stretching or contracting of the figures as well as of the curves to make them fit.

I see that this strikes a responsive chord. And, on reflection, there is no reason why it should not. For, after all, nature is not concerned about our analytical difficulties. Nature doesn't operate in order to enable us to get beautiful curves. As a matter of fact, the fitting of a geometric curve to actual observations is a problem that can be solved only approximately, and often only by a considerable degree of generosity.

SECRETARY WALLACE: Professor Cohen, assuming that there are a million orders of truth . . .

DR. COHEN: I don't know what that means. I know only one kind of truth.

SECRETARY WALLACE: Let us go back to the pre-Copernican theories of astronomy. Those theories seemed to explain after a fashion the appropriate observations of that time.

DR. COHEN: That is right.

SECRETARY WALLACE: Advancing with that procedure, there is, of course, always the danger of directing the insight of the mind over the facts; there is always the danger that that particular order of truth, which may be a primitive order of truth, will be embraced over too long a period, especially if it is reinforced by colleges or by the church or government or other institutions.

DR. COHEN: Certainly. That is perfectly true.

SECRETARY WALLACE: I see, therefore, a certain amount of danger in your concept; although in some respects it runs entirely contrary to the Nazi doctrine of truth, yet I can see how your application could easily lend it comfort as well.

DR. COHEN: Well, my answer to that is the one I gave before. The only cure for hardened theory is logic, which enables us to see that the theory we propound is not the only possible one. Logic enables us to raise the question, does the theory satisfactorily explain the facts, or will other theories explain the facts just as well or better? That is the only cure that we have against hardened theory. Without it there is no cure at all, since we all see what we expect to see whether it is there or not—and we assume as facts that which we are too lazy or unable to question. What you call attention to is a very serious danger. But the only way to overcome it, it seems to me, is to be aware that many of our assumed facts are but theories. If you are aware that your assumption as to what are the facts involve a theory, then you ask what other theories are available and whether they may not explain the facts much better. More important still, in actual scientific research, it is well to ask whether another theory or point of view would not enable us to open up new fields better than the existent theory. The man who is on the firing line of science is not merely concerned with explaining the facts that exist—he wants to find something. Now some theories give you a better approach to seeing and finding things than others. For instance, on the theory that electricity acts at a distance there is no reason for looking for electric waves or for an apparatus that will create them; whereas, if you take the theory of Faraday, then you have some sort of clue to electric waves, and along that line you may find some phenomena; in fact, electric waves were discovered.

SECRETARY WALLACE: But that makes necessary a certain number of scientists who are always questioning the complete system which has hitherto been set up on the theory that this whole system, perhaps going back for a thousand years, may be falsely based from the standpoint of concrete truth.

DR. COHEN: That is right.

SECRETARY WALLACE: And who is going to back the scientist like that? He is a sure troublemaker.

DR. COHEN: He is! And I think the genuine scientist must always expect to be in trouble. Things excellent are not attained without trouble.

DR. TUCKERMAN: Dr. Cohen, I had a hard time trying to follow you in your statement about verification and confirmation. Look back over the history. I have read Newton (incidentally, in the original) and followed his corpuscular theory of light. I have followed the later developments, and have seen the wave theory come in and partially go out. The wave theory was at that time more stimulating to further research than any other. However, it was not verified any more than Newton's corpuscular theory was verified, for today we know that Newton, with his corpuscles, and his fits, was nearer to our present thought about light than were Huyghens, Young, and Fresnel.[4]

[4] From Newton's *Opticks* (1704), Book II, Part III, Prop. XII. "DEFINITION. The returns of the disposition of any Ray to be reflected I will call its *Fits of Easy Reflection;* and those of its disposition to be trans-

DR. COHEN: I should not admit that.

DR. TUCKERMAN: Because today light is both corpuscles and waves, or shall we say with Newton, corpuscles and fits.

DR. COHEN: That doesn't mean that Fresnel is wrong, though.

DR. TUCKERMAN: No, but Newton's ideas contained more of our modern thought than Fresnel's. Because Huyghens and Young and Fresnel's way of thinking was at the time a more stimulating way of thinking than Newton's is no reason for saying that it was more verified than his. Similarly I want to mention again action at a distance. We can take all of our field theory, and can convert it back by means of retarded potentials to the old theory of action at a distance. We do not ordinarily do so because in most cases thinking in terms of the field theory is a more fruitful way of thinking— easier, better. There are, however, still some problems in which the old theory of action at a distance gives us a clearer picture and makes our thinking easier. Where, then, does the distinction between verification and confirmation come in?

DR. COHEN: Well, in the first place I don't agree with your statement concerning the bearing of Fresnel's experiments. I think that Fresnel's experiments did show that Huyghens' theory was better than Newton's in the form in which Newton originally propounded it. If you look upon light as consisting of material corpuscles, then the question of diffraction becomes relevant and Newton's theory does not explain the phenomenon that Fresnel's experiments reveal. The experiments of Young and Fresnel do point to a difficulty which Newton's original theory cannot overcome, and therefore as between the wave theory and Newton's corpuscular theory, Newton's theory was definitely refuted. Hence, according to the view of verification that I am propounding, the wave theory was verified in the sense that it could not only explain

mitted, its *Fits of Easy Transmission* and the space it passes between every return and the next return, the *Interval of its Fits*."

everything explained by the Newtonian theory but also certain phenomena that the latter could not.

Now, today we are in a different position. Today we don't talk any more about light consisting of material particles. Today we talk of electrons and their fields, and as the electron is both a particle and a wave, it satisfies both the corpuscular and the wave theory. This illustrates the point I made before, that when we verify a theory we do not prove it, but only show it to be better than the available alternative theory. Now in the state of knowledge of the latter part of the nineteenth century the wave theory with its ether was the best available theory. It explained phenomena of light and electricity better than the corpuscular theory. But with the abandonment of the ether and the new conception of the electron and photon you have elements of both theories, Newton's and Huyghens', and an entirely different situation.

DR. TUCKERMAN: Must we give up and say Newton was wrong?

DR. COHEN: Yes, we should say that Newton was wrong. And he was wrong in considering mass as an absolute constant, and that if we kept on increasing the force acting on it we could increase the resulting velocity indefinitely. To the extent that Newton assumed such a thing he was definitely wrong. That is why we have non-Newtonian mechanics today; it rests on experimental evidence as well as on the relativity theory.

DR. SEEGER: I was just wondering if perhaps there aren't different uses of the word "theory." I always like to use the word "theory" in the sense of its root, *theoria,* which enables you to see a few things. Now, Newton standing at a certain position saw a few things. If we go back today and stand in that same position we see the same view, and Einstein has another view.

DR. COHEN: A wider view.

DR. SEEGER: And if we can get a still higher point that will take everything in, then we have the best theory of all.

Dr. Cohen: That is it. That is precisely what I am maintaining.

Dr. Seeger: May I ask you an embarrassing question? I am going to rely upon your sense of humor. You said last night a very true thing, that the world is full of myths and superstitions. I have always thought that probably we shall never get rid of them. It is like weeds, when you get rid of one kind another kind comes up. You were suggesting that we get rid of the myth that Galileo had propounded the well-publicized experiment on falling bodies, and I agree that from Professor Lane Cooper's work, and from what I have been able to read through the translation of Galileo's work, that there is no direct evidence of that experiment. I wonder, however, if we are not putting up another myth when we say that the experiment has never been performed.

Dr. Cohen: All the experiments of this kind indicate what was pointed out by a man that lived long before Galileo, namely, Lucretius. Lucretius pointed out that if you take two things, a stone and a coin, and drop them in water, they won't sink at the same rate, and he explained that this is due to the resistance of the medium. Now I take it that air is a medium, and like water will offer a greater proportionate resistance to a lighter body than to a heavier body. I assume, therefore, that it is accepted by all physicists that in the air a lighter body will take a longer time to fall than a heavier body. Einstein in his book on the *Evolution of Physics* refers to the supposed experiment from the Tower of Pisa, and says that it proved that objects come down at the same time. When I last saw him, I said, "Dr. Einstein, how can you say that? You know that the air is a medium, and that a heavier body overcomes the resistance of a medium more than a lighter body." To which he said, "Of course you are right."

Please remember that I don't say that the experiment from the Tower of Pisa didn't take place, but I say that if the experiment did take place it wouldn't have proved what the books say it did; theoretically it should have shown that in the air all other things being equal the heavier body comes down first.

DR. WINTERS: Dr. Cohen, I gathered from your discussion that you recognized the weakness in our scientific procedure due to a lack of historical background and that we may be stronger in technique than in other important factors. Consider the mental attitude of weighing evidence. That brings us back to the preparation for scientific work. Is the historical background more essential or the development of curiosity through training? What can be done toward developing this attitude toward scientific research and so on?

DR. COHEN: I should say curiosity is a function of two factors. One is native endowment. Some people have no curiosity; they are listless intellectually. All sorts of things happen and they are not interested. The capacity to be interested, I think, is native. On the other hand, the element of training is not to be overlooked. I think that all normal children and many animals such as dogs show some curiosity. Children show their curiosity by asking all sorts of questions. Education either represses or encourages this inclination. The parents and teachers who do not like to admit their ignorance give some fake answer which confuses the child or gets the latter into the habit of being satisfied with verbalisms. Sometimes things like that happen in the universities.

When I was young I taught elementary mathematics in the high school department of my college, and I had a textbook which pretended to prove that every equation had a root. I knew enough mathematics to be familiar with two attempts of Gauss to prove that proposition. The great Gauss found it difficult. But the author of my textbook blithely tried to prove it to freshmen in a few lines. Needless to add, it was a phony proof. It is that sort of thing that kills curiosity. It is like giving a stone to a hungry man; it will kill his hunger if he swallows it.

What you say about techniques is, I think, very important. It is important to realize that scientists are not likely to make many grave mistakes in the ordinary laboratory procedures. For their techniques are worked out before them, and so long as they go on the beaten path they cannot go far wrong. But when it comes to tackling new problems you need more background. That is why I think it is a great misfortune for students to begin to specialize too early. A young fellow makes up his mind to become a botanist and he doesn't take courses in mathematics or astronomy, theoretical physics, or geology. Well, he is not likely to become a great botanist. He may be able to do routine things well, but if he wants to be creative he ought to have his mind awake. I don't say his mind will necessarily be awakened by the actual course given in physics at his college. He may be better off not to take it. But the principle I am asserting is that if the botanist has the kind of mind that is awake to larger possibilities, he will look at problems in botany from a wider point of view and get the wider perspective that you have indicated, and see new possibilities where other men will not.

Take a concrete example: Einstein worked out the special theory of relativity. Then there was a problem before him: how on earth can it be made to fit in with the effect of acceleration? If you are on a train that is moving uniformly, the principle of relativity can be illustrated. But suppose the engineer puts on the brakes or suppose he speeds up. Well, your coffee spills or things behave differently, and that is an experimental fact. How can you reconcile that with the principle of relativity? The ordinary man of science could not get around such a difficulty. But an Einstein, with the genius for real thought, is not stumped. After all what is a fact? We call that a fact which we take for granted to be involved in our sense experience and which we explain in certain terms; and the question may be raised: Can we interpret the supposed facts somewhat differently? That is what Einstein did and arrived at the general theory of relativity. May I give you another example? I took a course once in psychology with Professor C. A. Strong. In this course Strong expounded with great thoroughness his theory of panpsychism. In the last hour of the term he said to us, "Gentlemen, there is one difficulty with my theory which I haven't taken up, and that is that it doesn't fit the facts." A few of us laughed, as you do, but he quietly added:

"After all, what are the facts? The facts of psychology are those data of experience which we interpret in the light of the currently accepted ideas. But since I reject these ideas, the theory which I hold cannot agree with the customary interpretations. Therefore, what I have to do is to take all the data of psychology and show how they do fit into my theory; and that requires a course by itself."

DR. DEMING: Dr. Cohen, yesterday I understood you to make the statement that few scientists know what the nature of science really is and I dare say that is true and I don't feel competent to judge, but I want to ask: Do you think a man can be a good scientist and not have an intuitive feeling either by training or native ability for the nature of science?

DR. COHEN: If a man hasn't an intuitive insight into problems and where they lead to he cannot do first-rate work. But that is different from having a clearly articulated idea of what the whole thing is about.

DR. DEMING: Would you explain?

DR. COHEN: Well, let me say this: we must get back to the principle of routine versus the principle of initiative. In a great deal of scientific work there is much routine. Now in routine work you don't need to know what is going on outside of your narrow field. If you have the training, if you have the technique, you know almost instinctively what you have to do. No biologist, for instance, will commit the fallacy of Freudian psychologists, of having no control to check his observation. Every biologist "instinctively" knows enough to use controls, in the sense that it has become a habit. But when he comes to a new problem, and the ordinary analogies which have been built up in the course of his routine fail, the old habit or technique is no longer sufficient. One must have a wider view to see new possibilities. Thus it isn't every competent scientist who makes great discoveries or opens new paths. Wider views stimulate the imagination to see new analogies not seen in narrow fields.

I don't know whether I have made my point clear, but I should like to.

DR. DEMING: Yes, thank you. I should like to ask another question. It may be clear off the subject, but I should like to get your opinion: Is mathematics a science and is physics a science? How do they differ? Are they both sciences?

DR. COHEN: Because the term science is one of praise, those who quarrel about the word are usually interested in the prestige that goes with it. But the mathematician deals with a subject that is too well established and too absorbing in interest to make him care whether you call it science or not. It is the sociologist who, not having the advantage of such a definite subject matter, is so much concerned in defending his claim to be called a scientist.

But I want to answer the question. Let me put it this way: If we are interested in a subject, we can change its name. Let us then drop the word "science" and speak of the kind of knowledge for which there is evidence, that is to say, views or assertions that are not arbitrary but for which there is some support. Now, if you regard science as the ascertaining of propositions for which there is evidence or proof, no one can deny that mathematics is a science. If, for instance, you assume Euclid's axioms, is it or is it not true that four circles can be tangent to each other, or that there are only five regular polyhedrons? There can be no doubt that we can prove that it is impossible, absolutely impossible, for Euclid's axioms to be true and the proposition that there are only five regular polyhedrons to be false. That is the kind of knowledge that we acquire when we study geometry. Now if you have a grudge against mathematics, you can define the word "science" so as to exclude mathematics. But there is no doubt that mathematics is a science in the sense that it is demonstrable knowledge.

Of course, mathematics differs from physics. For in physics we are not satisfied merely to have the kind of knowledge which informs us that if certain premises are true, certain conclusions must follow. In physics, we want to know whether certain things are so, whether actual observation will fit into our axioms or primitive propositions. In other words, the physicist wants to know something about the actual world and not merely about possibilities. He not only applies or uses mathematics, but checks up the result of his deduction by observation on nature. He thus has verifiable knowledge and that is surely what we ordinarily mean by science.

DR. LAURITZEN: Yes, but you said check up the mathematical equations, and that is just the point I am getting at. The mathematical equations are true if the man hasn't made a mistake—perfectly good based on certain postulates following certain rules; his equations are true whether he observes anything to correspond with them or not.

DR. COHEN: I would not quite put it that way. Equations other than identities are not true by themselves; i.e., equations that refer to existing things and formulate laws of physics or of other natural science are true only if what they assert is as asserted. We must not forget the difference between the point of view of the mathematician and that of the physicist. The former deals with necessary relations between all possible entities. If a man like Einstein begins with an equation like that which expresses the photo-electric law and deduces certain consequences, the process of deduction is pure mathematics. But as physicist he isn't satisfied with that. To the physicist, equations describe states of nature and he wants to know whether the deduced consequences hold in fact. Mathematics alone cannot tell him whether the law of gravitation, the law of conservation of energy, or any other particular law is true or not. That is a question of fact, and that means, ultimately, whether the observations of nature fit into our mathematical equations.

DR. LAURITZEN: Since one can't tell from the study of mathematics whether these equations are true that brings up the question of whether physics and mathematics are the same thing.

DR. COHEN: They are not the same, obviously; for while mathematics is a part of physics, it is not the whole of physics, and therefore the two cannot be identical. I would go further and say that if we enlarge, as we must, our concept of mathematics and define it as Benjamin Peirce (1809-1880) did as the art of drawing the necessary implication of our assumptions, then every study is scientific to the extent that it is mathematical. But mathematics is surely not the whole of natural science.

DR. ENGLUND: You said that if such and such is true, that is, if our assumptions are true, then what follows must necessarily be true. Isn't that also an assumption?

DR. COHEN: No, it isn't an assumption in the ordinary sense. There is a difference. The ordinary assumption has an alternative, but the assumption of logic has no genuine alternative. Take, for instance, Euclid's axiom that from a point outside a straight line only one parallel can be drawn. That is an assumption. To be sure, for over two thousand years it was generally regarded as self-evident. But when you examine it logically you see it has two possible alternatives: no parallel lines can be drawn, or more than one can be drawn. To a genuinely logical proposition, however, there is no alternative. To the proposition, *it will rain tomorrow,* there is an alternative. Not so to the proposition: *it will either rain or not.* The logical laws of identity and contradictions cannot be really doubted. For when you express the doubt you have already assumed the laws of logic to make your statement say what it does and not its contradictory.

DR. RANDS: May that not be just merely a product of mind?

DR. COHEN: That wouldn't make any difference in regard to its meaning or validity.

DR. ENGLUND: Does that mean that there isn't necessarily one?

DR. COHEN: No, the question is not merely one of psychology, of how the mind works, or whether you or I in fact see certain things. The question is a logical one, whether any doubt to a strictly logical proposition can be formulated. A concrete example may make it clear. John Stuart Mill, with the courage of his empiricist confusion, said that two plus two may be four for us, but might be five on some other planet. That is concretely the kind of issue which you are raising. What is the answer to Mill? It is simply to make the distinction that you made before. If you mean that two drops of water and two drops of alcohol will make four drops of the same size, then you don't need to go to Mars to see that that is dubious.[5] If you take equal volumes of gases far enough away from their critical points you will find two plus two equals *two*, because the gases interfuse and the two have the same volume as either one alone at the same temperature and pressure. But if you mean by two plus two what the mathematician means, that is to say, assume that there are any two entities that are distinct, and two other equally distinct entities of any kind, then we can show that it has no meaning to say they might as such be five. Every mathematical proposition exhausts the field of possibility.

DR. ENGLUND: Professor Cohen, yesterday you touched upon the social field in the course of your lecture and I should like to ask you a question bearing on it. I understood you to say that the progress of science in general depends upon the capacity for self-correction.

DR. COHEN: That is right.

DR. ENGLUND: Now, under the totalitarian society there

[5] The reader may wish to examine what C. I. Lewis says on this very point in his *Mind and the World-Order* (Chas. Scribner's Sons, New York, 1929), p. 250.

presumably would be in many fields less opportunity for self-correction. Would you care to express yourself then as to the general implication of relative degrees of totalitarianism upon the progress of science?

DR. COHEN: Well, let me put the problem in a most general way. The distinctive trait of all science is precisely that instead of trying to squelch doubt by force, it encourages it as far as possible. The primitive habit is that of authority and reiteration which parents and poor pedagogues illustrate when they are asked embarrassing questions. Communities generally try to suppress doubt concerning accepted ways when just doubt raises fear or irritation. In the absence of the latter, we ignore the man, call him a fool, an idiot, or something of that sort.

If somebody wants to disprove the proposition that in Euclidean geometry the square of the hypotenuse is equal to the sum of the squares of the other two sides, we don't get much annoyed because we know perfectly well we can prove it to anyone who is willing to listen and understand. But if somebody questions something that we can't prove and about which we profess to be certain, then we get irritated. You can see that everywhere. Human certainty generally varies inversely in proportion to the amount of knowledge. Take the ordinary citizen. Of what things is he most certain? Surely not of the things of which he has most information. Suppose he is interested in the lard market and we ask him the prospects. He will be cautious and give us qualified answers, because he knows something about it. But ask him questions on politics, or religion, and he is one hundred per cent certain, because he knows nothing to the contrary. And when you begin to question him on these matters he gets excited because of the fear that he might not be able to prove he is not prepared to abandon.

Science as a self-corrective system can abandon any one proposition when there is evidence against it, since it does so by its own method and so maintains its continuity. But

[81]

the unscientific have no such way and hence must cling to their assertions by reiteration and suppressing any opponent or doubter. The nonscientific attitude, however, breaks down in heterogeneous or rapidly changing societies. Imagine, for instance, a child born in an Arabian village. He hears everyone say five times a day, "There is no God but Allah and Mohammed is His prophet." To him that is as much of a fact as electric currents are to us. We all believe there are electric currents and we pity anybody who questions that. But suppose the Arab leaves his village and goes to Europe. He meets people who don't believe in Mohammed. Then he is perplexed. He begins to reflect or analyze—that is what we call the disintegration of ideas.

How can that disquiet which comes from disintegration of ideas be dealt with? Of course, one way is to suppress or even kill all the people who doubt. It is a great mistake to think we don't get unanimity by killing off those who don't agree with us. I think human history shows that that is a fairly successful method so far as human efforts ever are successful. For instance, classical paganism was actually suppressed, in its outer forms at least, and thus eliminated by force. But that is not the method of science. The method of science takes the bull by the horns and says: "No, we are not going to suppress any doubt. On the contrary, we will try to raise as many questions as we can, because if we question everything we shall very often extend the limits of our knowledge, and within those limits we shall be able to build up something enduring or at least capable of continuous growth." Now the disadvantage of science is that it never gives us absolute results, because being a self-corrective system, you must keep the thing open for the possibility of correction. Such an attitude is very distasteful to most people. Most people like to sleep on a pillow that has no doubt in it. The result, therefore, is that this attitude of scientific procedure is very distasteful, and human beings find it hard to keep it up. The progress of science is thus by no means assured. It goes contrary to our inclination. Human inclination finds it easier to rely on authority.

It is a great mistake to think government rests on force. It rests upon the need of people to be governed. And the Good Book illustrates it in the story of how Saul became the first king of Israel. You remember Saul was looking for his father's asses which had strayed. And when they decided to make him king, he tried to hide among the wagons, but they sought him out and insisted upon making him king. That is a psychologically very true account of the nature of government. People dislike not only anarchy, but also to have to decide for themselves. For that involves responsibility and thought which is always painful. Those of us who have tried it know that.

MR. GLICK: Is that the reason that you were so discouraged about the application of the scientific method to social problems?

DR. COHEN: I am not discouraged. I merely want to look fearlessly at the facts as they actually exist. Science makes progress because it isn't absolutely certain. In those fields in which we are absolutely certain there can be no progress. If you have the complete truth, then to that extent there can be no change for the better. Science means progress because it is constantly correcting itself, and therefore there can always be more correction. This holding yourself in balance and saying, "So far the thing has worked, but we must be prepared to modify it," is very distasteful to people who want to know the final results of science. That is why popular science is largely mythologic. What people demand of popular science is not the evidence that is necessary to qualify the validity of any proposition. People don't care about evidence. What they want is the story or romance of science.

Now anybody who tries to formulate any result of science without the qualifications within which it is true, is of course producing a romance, and it seems to me that men like Eddington and others are trying to persuade people to think that they understand the quantum theory, which no one possibly can who doesn't know enough mathematics. Nevertheless, it is easy to persuade people that they do understand, for it flatters their vanity. They are anxious to believe it, and there is nothing that succeeds so well as giving people what they are anxious to have. Thus you get pseudo-science.

And here we come back to your point that the totalitarian powers have a great advantage over the democratic powers, because the democratic powers ultimately assume that human beings can reason and can weigh evidence for changed doctrines or changed policies. The totalitarian powers assume that the people are either averse to or incapable of thought, and prefer their accustomed ways. Generally speaking, they are thus apt to succeed in the routine of life. Government thus always triumphs over anarchy. But there are periods of stress when the good order breaks down because it is a hindrance to the better. That was clearly demonstrated in the war of 1914-1918 between Germany and the Allies. Germany was highly disciplined and the people trusted their commanders implicitly. But when these commanders proved in error, when the final victory in the summer of 1918 did not come, the German people collapsed.

Now in democratic governments there is always an opposition, and the opposition encourages distrust of the government to a certain extent, and people are not so completely surprised that the government can't deliver the goods all the time. Hence defeats did not so readily break the morale of the French and English.

Dr. ENGLUND: Would you conclude, then, that on the long pull democracy is more efficient than totalitarianism, although on the short pull you would grant the advantage to the latter?

Dr. COHEN: If we last long enough we shall outlast the dictators, yes.

Dr. BLAISDELL: Professor Cohen, what you said about sociologists a while back in a way answers the question I am going to put to you, but still I am going to ask it anyway. It is very common these days for the so-called man in the street, and moreover a good many people who are supposed to be intelligent, to refer to a certain body of knowledge as the social sciences. In the first place are we presumptuous in using the appellation "social science" to apply to that field of knowledge? And in the second place, does the habitual use of it, and popular use of that phrase encourage generally greater expectation from the people who are studying in that field than we have a right to expect from them?

DR. COHEN: I would answer the second question categorically in the affirmative. I should think that the use of the term social science tends to produce a pretension that is not justified and therefore inimical to the very spirit of science. The false pretense or expectation is aroused especially through the use of technical terminology.

One of the great revolutions in the intellectual history of mankind occurred at the end of the seventeenth and the beginning of the eighteenth century, and that was the change from the use of Latin to the vernacular as the language of the learned. Even in Harvard College, I am informed, all the recitations were in Latin up to the Year of Grace, 1828. Now, when you speak Latin you are a learned man. You don't have to do anything more. But when you translate the thing into ordinary English then you must say something in order to keep up your prestige as a learned man. That is what happened in some German and Scottish universities at the end of the seventeenth and at the beginning of the eighteenth century when men like Thomasius, Hutcheson, and Adam Smith began to lecture in the vernacular. Thomasius was almost killed for it by his fellows who saw the danger. But the old professors were needlessly afraid. For by substituting technical terminology for the vernacular they produced the same old situation over again. The ordinary man who wants to know what life is reads Herbert Spencer, and when he is told it is the sum of the vital activities or functions he feels that he has found the secret and he is satisfied. Or when he is told that there are processes of integration or reintegration,

[85]

he gets the impression that he is in the presence of profound science. Starched terminology gives one the feeling of being in high intellectual society. In that way, I think, the false appearance of the term "science" is a real hindrance to progress in actual knowledge. We must get rid of the appearance of saying something when, in point of fact, we are engaged in empty formalities.

Most human conversation is really meaningless, and it isn't supposed to have any meaning provided it conforms to the proper form. It is just ceremonial gesture.

But to get to your first question, I should say it is a great mistake to try to rule out all social studies as unscientific because of the false pretense on the part of some who haven't any insight or subject matter and therefore have to quarrel about their terminology. I think there is a great deal of genuine critical knowledge resting upon good evidence in most of the social studies, and I would make a strong plea for history as a science, not in a sense that it sets up laws (that is nonsense, since history deals with individual facts) but in the precise sense that it deals with evidence critically. Did Louis XVI conspire with the *émigré* nobles? The scientific historian examines the available evidence and considers the various possible interpretations and the difficulties they involve. I say that men of that type deserve the name of scientist just as much as geologists or naturalists of the type of Darwin.

I should then answer your first question by saying that there are real fields of science in the realm of social fact. The man who has an eye for facts, whether it be about human beings, stones, or anything else, the man who asks, "Is it so?" and "Can it be verified?" has the essence of all science, provided he follows the critical methods of proof and verification. The difficulty is not only that social facts are more complicated and thus have a high variability, but that we are under pressure and in a hurry to produce results. But genuine scientific results that will bear criticism and withstand the attrition of time cannot be produced in a hurry. They have to be submitted to all sorts of tests. Hence those who have the genuine scientific spirit always resent being hurried. They tell at Johns Hopkins that President Gilman who was very anxious to get the men on his faculty to publish books went one day to Rowland's laboratory and asked, "Dr. Rowland, have you published anything recently or are you contemplating any publication?" Rowland then said, "Go away, go away. Don't you see I am busy?" Now, I think Rowland, who was one of our greatest physicists, had the right point of view. He was engaged in a problem and he was not going to publish things because the university needed credit.

Let me mention something that has a bearing on both your questions. When in the meeting of the Royal Society the result of the expedition to test the Einstein theory was announced, and Newton's law of gravity was thus in a limited sense overthrown, one man is reported to have gone out shaking his head dolefully, "And to think of it, that the Royal Society should listen to a paper attacking Newton who was once its president!" Now, that man seems to me to express the essence of all that science is not. Science was perfectly willing to honor Einstein, who was a German and a Jew, and to overthrow in part the theory of the national hero, Newton. Science is willing to honor the innovator because science doesn't depend upon loyalty to an accepted doctrine, but is willing to overthrow any doctrine for any other for which there is better evidence.

Now if we have that attitude in the social field we can make progress. But what do we have? In the social field we find that certain doctrines are taboo and certain doctrines are hallowed. How many of us do not recoil at the words "Bolshevism," "Communism" or "Fascism," "free love," "atheism," or fail to be thrilled by the words "democratic," "progressive," etc. But since these words are vague and cover multitudes of different things, free inquiry is hindered by the emotional attitude.

MR. BEAN: I couldn't help but try to apply your suggestion

[87]

with respect to the desire to get results with accuracy in the very narrow field of administrative economics. A very specific example, let us say, might be where the question arises, what volume of industrial activities is required to give us an eighty-billion-dollar national income? Now some of us working together can answer that question within twenty-four hours. We place together certain bits of information and we approximate the answer. We feel intuitively that the answer will be within five per cent correct, that we might have to have a fifty per cent increase in production—forty-five per cent to fifty-five per cent, or something of that nature, and for administrative purposes that answer is sufficient. On the other hand, you will find throughout the government circles the attitude of the economists that they mustn't be pressed for an answer today or tomorrow, and that if we set up a dozen people to answer that question perhaps within the next six months we should have the exact answer.

Now, isn't there some danger of the economist and the sociologist trying to be scientific in your sense, while meanwhile the parade will pass by and there will be no need of his answer by the time he gets it, though a ninety per cent answer would have been sufficient if delivered on time?

DR. COHEN: What you say is perfectly true. But we must distinguish between two different questions. One is how to live, and the other is what is the nature of things. Now, unfortunately we have to live today before we can find out the nature of things. What you are calling attention to is the fact, for instance, that the government has to function today, and that the true result of its action might not be found in six months—indeed, it might never be found. Consider the exact causes of bodily locomotion. What is it really that makes the nerve "conduct" and the muscles contract? The question hasn't been completely answered as yet. But that is no reason for my not walking. When you have to go somewhere you walk along and don't bother about the scientific problem of nerves and muscles. Science is not always a pre-condition for

[88]

other human activities. Science satisfies primarily, I should say, an intellectual interest.

Now man is not only an animal that consumes food or surrounds himself with various kinds of clothes and buildings, but he also has this curiosity and wants to find out things. Man's various desires sometimes clash. The desire to know is one thing and the desire to make the government function is another thing. Now I do not believe with Plato that government should be run by philosophers or scientists. Government must satisfy other demands than that of human curiosity. Although no government can really function well unless it does appeal to the imagination of its people, it has a number of daily chores, which must be done whether our knowledge is adequate or not. Government cannot stop its functions to wait until we find out all that is involved in a proposed action. That we may never be able to find out.

But that is no excuse for saying that something is science because we do not have time to find out whether it is true. What is inexcusable is not the fact that we have to act on inadequate knowledge, but that philosophers put up sad limitations as the road to, or substance of, the truth. To say that where we can't get the full truth, we should believe that which we know isn't true, is a perversion or corruption of human intelligence against which genuine science is a protest. "We live forwards and we think backwards," said the Danish philosopher, Kierkegaard. We are born into the world before we think, and it takes some time before we learn to do so, but meanwhile we want to live. So what you say is perfectly true, the government has to live. The streets have to be kept clean. Certain individuals have to be prevented from indulging natural instincts for mischief. All of these things have to be done, and those scientists who think they can solve all problems before we have to act are overoptimistic.

THE DISTINCTION BETWEEN
THE MENTAL AND
THE PHYSICAL

THE FOLLOWING CONSIDERATIONS can make no claim as a contribution to a baffling subject. My philosophic studies have been somewhat restricted to the logic of mathematical physics and applied ethics, and on epistemologic problems I can speak only with an innocence which I trust may not be regarded as too childish. But being drafted into this discussion, I prefer to be guided by my loyalty to this association rather than by any confidence that what I have to say will be of great service to my more mature colleagues.

In answer to the question put to us, "Is the division of entities present or involved in experience into the two reciprocally exclusive classes of the mental and physical to be retained?" I wish to maintain that while we must, by all means, keep the distinction between the mental and the physical, we must reject the view that they are mutually or reciprocally exclusive.

Two substances or classes, *A* and *B,* which are distinct, may bear to each other any one of four relations. First, *A* may be part of *B;* second, *B* may be part of *A;* third, *A* and *B* may be mutually exclusive; and fourth, *A* and *B* may be overlapping or intersecting. If *A* denotes the physical and *B* the mental realm, the first three views may be called, respectively, mentalism (subjective idealism), materialism, and dualism. For reasons which will be clearer later on, the fourth view may be called neutral monism.

1. IDEALISM (MENTALISM)

THE THESIS that all is mental, and that what we call physical is only a certain selected portion thereof, is a doctrine that few nowadays clearly and expressly maintain. But philosophies which explain everything as made up of a stuff called experience, and conceive experience as psychological or mental, lead to the same result. At any rate, this type of idealism is expressly found in systems as diverse as those of Fichte and Schopenhauer, and is indubitably implied by the language of Locke, Berkeley, and Hume. The great historic argument for it is Locke's assertion that "the mind hath no other immediate object but its own ideas." The metaphysical doctrine, then, ⌐ that everything exists in the mind, finds support in the epistemologic doctrine that the mind can know only its own modifications. The latter doctrine, like most others which have been widely assumed as self-evident, has received astonishingly little evidence or proof in its favor. It has a certain verbal cogency so long as we do not distinguish between sensation or ideas as processes and as objects sensed or thought of. Since that distinction has been insisted upon by Mr. G. E. Moore, in his epoch-making paper on the "Refutation of Idealism," few have come out openly in defense of the proposition that the *esse* of things is their *percipi*.[1] Even writers who call themselves idealists, like A. E. Taylor, have pointed out that the doctrine that nothing can be known except by an idea of it involves a vicious infinite regress. If, on the other hand, ideas can be known directly, why cannot things also be known directly? It is not, however, necessary to argue this doctrine. It is sufficient to point out that the proposition that all is mental, like other assertions about *all things* is futile. If everything is mental, no specific differentia are left for that which we ordinarily call our inner or mental life, our hopes, emotions, etc. By resolving physical objects into ideas, we are still left with a difference between ideas like spoons with which we eat, and ideas in our mind only.

In thus pointing out the scientific futility of monistic subjective idealism, I do not mean to deny its tremendous social

[1] *Mind,* Vol. 28, 1903.

and religious significance in the history of civilization. It offered a powerful support for the revolutionary individualism which broke the bonds of external authority in political and religious life. It destroyed the belief in the divine power of kings and priests. Above all, it offered a vital compensation to the emotional depression of the Copernican discovery that man's abode is not the center of the universe. "Your body," idealism said, "may be located on a tiny speck of dust, but the whole stellar system, after all, exists only in your mind." That doctrine, however, had no effect on the study of astronomy or on any other physical science. Indeed, in its phenomenalistic or sensational form, as represented by Mach, Ostwald, and Pearson, this monistic idealism would have proved a positive hindrance to progress in physics if it were not for the fortunate fact that it has had no influence on those engaged in physical research. For by insisting that physical objects are constituted by sensational elements only, these thinkers would expressly rule out such hypotheses as those relating to atoms, electrons, etc., which have in recent years transformed physical science. It is true that there are serious dangers in multiplying hypothetical entities, which led the greatest of all physicists to say *"hypotheses non fingo."* Nevertheless, the fact remains that the hypothetical method as embodied in works of men like Faraday, Kelvin, Boltzman, Maxwell, and J. J. Thomson has been an integral part of the life of physical science.

2. MATERIALISM

A SIMILAR logical or scientific futility attaches to materialism. It is not necessary to refute the resolution to call everything matter or body. We need only point out that the science of physics treats only of definite kinds of bodies, gases, solids, etc., and excludes from these such entities as wishes, imaginings, and beliefs. If entities of the latter kind could enter the physical causal series, modern science would be impossible. It would be indistinguishable from witchcraft and magic.

3. EXCLUSIVE DUALISM

IN OUR ORDINARY daily experience, the handling of spatial things is of such preponderant importance that there naturally arises a tendency to reification, to regard all objects of consideration as if they were mutually exclusive *things*. This tendency is reinforced by the philosopher's love of simplicity, since the relation of mutual exclusion is the simplest relation between two different classes. This is embodied in the ordinary phraseology in which the problem is stated, for example, "the external world," "the contents of the mind," and the use of the dangerous little word *in*. Now, it seems obvious that externality is a relation which we apply only to physical objects. One physical thing is external to another physical thing when they occupy different portions of space. In what sense, then, can the whole physical world be external to a mind which is by hypothesis not physical at all? It is not too much to assert that the whole modern epistemologic problem arises from the fact that, having conceived the mental and the physical as two mutually exclusive substances, it becomes difficult to express the simple fact that physical objects are knowable and that knowledge is an act of the mind. The epistemologic doctrine, according to which we know, not objects directly, but only copies of them in the mind, is but a device whereby the hard and fast Cartesian dualism may be maintained, by preventing the physical world itself from entering into the mind. All our modern classical doctrines of sensations, images, etc., are but steps in this construction. I am not competent to pass any judgment on the psychological controversy as to whether we do or do not have sensations or images. But even if we do have sensations that are not simply qualities of physical objects, and even if we never think without having images, it still seems to me demonstrably certain that we do know objects other than these sensations and images. When I know the binomial theorem, Occam's razor, the periodic law, the history of the Chinese political system, the fact that Poland is starving, or the supposed truth that nothing can be known except by experience, I may or may not have images of various kinds before the mind. But the objects known are not the images present, but things not sensibly present at all. Indeed, does not the dogma that nothing can be known except by an idea, sensation, or image of it, *presuppose* that we do know things of which there are sensations, images, or copies? Let us examine carefully the usual arguments for the dualistic position.

1. Ever since Hobbes, the existence of sense organs has been used as an argument that we perceive not the objects, but their phantasms, and that such phantasms are differently located in time and space from the objects known. This account of the matter assumes that objects can be known as existing at a time different from the time of perception; but if this is admitted, the argument for the existence of images, ideas, or perceptual doubles of *all* things known is not at all necessary. We need only admit that we may make a false judgment as to the time position of certain objects, and that further knowledge may lead us to correct that judgment. This would mean that there is no ultimate dualism between objects known and objects perceived, but that in actual concrete perception there is a judgment element which may or may not be compatible with other judgments.

2. The view that erroneous physical objects have their seat in the mind only, seems to me to have been made the object of unanswerable objections by writers as different as Professors Sheldon and Holt. Briefly, the point is that what makes us judge an object or quality erroneous is incompatibility with other objects or qualities regarded as veridical. But such incompatibility exists only between objects in the same known universe. Forms such as round and square are incompatible,

but not round and heavy. If veridical objects existed in the physical realm and erroneous objects in the mental realm, and the two realms were exclusive, there could be no explanation of error.

3. Another mode in which the world is cut into a physical and a mental half is by assigning primary qualities to the former and secondary qualities to the latter. But the arguments by which this division has been supported since the days of Locke and Berkeley seem to me all indefensible. The argument is that since the same object appears hot to one hand and cold to another, the heat and cold cannot be qualities of the object, but must reside only in the mind. This is a *non sequitur*. *Prima facie,* it could prove only that the heat of the object depends on the hand or physical sense organ, and not on the mind. In point of fact, physics explains the variations of secondary qualities not by reference to mind, but by taking into account the physical structure of the medium and sense organ. Such variations are duplicated in physical instruments such as thermometers, cameras, etc. Nor is it true that this relativity is characteristic only of secondary qualities. It is also true of primary qualities such as the weight of the body, its velocity, and even some of its geometric properties, such as its projections. Indeed, there are few things on which physics is so certain as that the properties of physical objects depend on the system of objects in which they are placed. What qualities are to be regarded as primary is simply a problem of logical economy, as to what is the smallest number that must be assumed such that all other properties can be derived from them.

In general, if we remember that physical objects are knowable and that mental events take place under determinate physical conditions, it is difficult to see how one can maintain that "the antithesis between the mental and the physical is the most absolute antithesis within the realm of being." [2] Again,

[2] Professor Pratt, *The Journal of Philosophy,* Vol. XIII, p. 687.

if we maintain that things are not the direct objects of knowledge, and that what we know directly are percepts, images, and copies of things, then we have the hitherto unanswered question, What evidence do we have that these images, etc., *are* perfect copies? Direct comparison between things and our images would seem to be out of the question. It seems also that physical things have a more continuous existence than our intermittent ideas of them. Moreover, if we hold with Professor Pratt that spatial characteristics are in the mind, does it not follow that space itself must be in the mind, and if so, what becomes of our rigid dualism? There seems to me no escape from the logical fact that if we divide the total universe into two mutually exclusive classes or substances, one of these will have to be defined in purely negative terms; and all negative classes are essentially indefinite.

4. NEUTRAL MONISM [3]

THIS VIEW is not so much a solution to the problem how the mental and the physical are to be distinguished, as a doctrine how the question must be put, in order to make the answer significant. It insists that every system, physical or mental, is but a class or selection of neutral entities, and therefore can be defined only by the character of the fundamental principles or postulates of the system. The physical system is thus simply the class of entities to which our fundamental physical laws are applicable, and the psychological or mental system is the class of entities that meet certain other requirements, such as the capacity for specific response or what not. Such classes need not be mutually exclusive, and their precise interrelation must be the object of specific detailed study. Thus the whole physical system as an object known may be a single term in a mental series, while the mental series itself may be

[3] This point of view may as well be called pluralism.

[96]

attributed to a particular physical organism in time and space.

The question, how can the same entity be both in space and in consciousness, can be readily answered if we remember that the same thing can be in a number of different classes which are not mutually exclusive. A man may be in this room, in our association, and in a state of weariness, just as a man may be both a bankrupt and the author of a number of books on how to succeed in life.

The assertion that the mental and the physical are complexes of neutral entities may suggest the question, Where and when do these neutral entities exist, if not in the mind or in physical space? The answer is that anything may be said to exist in a given universe of discourse if it can be shown that it occupies a position therein. Thus Hamlet's melancholy and reflective character exists in Shakespeare's play, and the roots of equations exist in the number system. For in each case the particular entity can be shown to be demanded by the character of the system and of the other entities in it. So far as logic is applicable to both physics and psychology, neutral logical entities may be said to be parts both of the mental and of the physical series. But in so far as logic is distinguished from physics and psychology, the system of logical entities exists just as truly as the mental or physical systems exist. In our daily routine, problems as to existence in the physical system are of tremendous concern, but there is no evidence for the view that existence in the physical or mental system is in any way logically superior to that in the purely logical or other system. This may seem to degrade the term existence, and perhaps it does. But I believe that few habits would be more useful to philosophy than the habit of refusing to discuss whether certain entities exist, unless we ask exist how? or in what kind of a system?

As one looks over the recent literature of the mind-body controversy one cannot escape the feeling of the fruitlessness of it all. No important issues seem to grow out of or to depend on the different answers given to these problems. Hence there are today a growing number of thinkers who feel that the wisest course is to turn one's back on the whole business and face instead some of the more fruitful problems of philosophy which have been neglected for the sake of the epistemologic adventure. But if such turning one's back on that which our fellow workers regard as so important is not to be a mere manifestation of the wisdom of the ostrich, we must make certain that we have really eliminated the epistemologic difficulty *as an initial problem*. For woe be unto us if its protean ghost continues to haunt us! A sound epistemology can, therefore, certainly be useful in saving us a good deal of wasted effort and freeing our energies for genuinely fruitful problems.

BACON AND THE
INDUCTIVE METHOD

THE POPULAR BELIEF that Francis Bacon was the founder of modern science is so flagrantly in contradiction with all the facts of the history of science and so patently belied by the contents of Bacon's *Sylva Sylvarum* or the second book of his *Novum Organum* that it is most instructive to inquire how such an absurd belief ever gained currency among educated people. Unfortunately, however, the history of science previous to the seventeenth century is practically a closed book to those without both a classical and a scientific training. Even professional historians like Professor Robinson in his *Mind in the Making* seem to confirm the conventional fable that there was no science before the seventeenth century. Some indications, therefore, of the actual situation must be set down at the beginning.

1. No one can well dispute the fact that the great body of modern science rests on foundations already laid before the appearance of the *Novum Organum* in 1620. One needs only to mention the work of men like Copernicus, Kepler, Galileo, Stevinus and Gilbert in physics, or of Vesalius and Harvey in biology—omitting, for simplicity of argument, the great mathematicians from Archimedes to Tartaglia and Cardano. As all these men had long lines of predecessors as well as fellow workers, Bacon's repeated claim that there was altogether no well-established science based on experience before he came on the scene would in any other man be characterized as the claim of a crank or charlatan. Ignorance on Bacon's part is too generous an excuse. For he certainly must have known something of the epoch-making scientific work of Harvey, whom he knew personally. Does this not make it appear that Bacon's exaggerated claims to originality as to scientific method was the courtier's desire to gain prestige in the eyes of King James? Certainly his treatment of Gilbert's unpub-

lished writings which were entrusted to him did not show any disinterested desire for the spread of truth.

2. But whatever we may think of the fact and the motives for Bacon's ignoring the scientific work of his own and previous time, there is the still more significant fact that he positively opposed the great constructive scientific achievements of his day—the achievements on which subsequent scientific progress has in fact been based.

(a) He opposed, for instance, the Copernican astronomy which had received notable confirmation in his day through the scientific work of Kepler and Galileo. This fact is so glaring that many of Bacon's admirers have resorted to strange arguments to minimize it. They have attempted to do so either by softening the statement of the fact or by trying to find some justification for Bacon's position. Neither of these arguments, however, is in the least tenable.

Despite the beclouding efforts of Whewell and others, Bacon's opposition to the Copernican astronomy was emphatically explicit. In his *De Augmentis Scientiarum*,[1] he speaks of "the extravagant idea of diurnal motion of the earth, an opinion which we can demonstrate to be most false." This he repeats in the *Novum Organum*.[2]

Those who try to save the prestige of Bacon by claiming that in his day the evidence for the Copernican astronomy was inadequate, imply that Bacon's sense of evidence was superior to that of Kepler, Galileo, and Gilbert. But this cannot for a moment be tolerated by anyone familiar with the mathematical work of Kepler, with Galileo's demonstration of the phases of Venus and especially with the very flimsy character of the evidence which Bacon himself adduced for the older view. His boasted proof consisted of nothing else but the naïve repetition of the Aristotelian doctrine that "the eternal motion of revolution appears peculiar to the heavenly bodies, rest to this globe." [3]

[1] Book III, Ch. 4.   [2] Book I, Ch. 46; *cf.* Glob. Int., Ch. 6.
[3] *Novum Organum*, II, 35; *cf.* II, 36.

(b) Bacon also opposed the growing and fruitful method of explaining physical phenomena as far as possible in terms of mechanics. This method, begun by the ancient Greeks and developed by the Italians in the latter part of the sixteenth century, did not appeal to Bacon, who believed in *species spiritualis* as the explanation of sound and that the "human understanding is perverted by observing the power of mechanical arts." [4] Despite a few grudgingly approving words, Gilbert's genuinely experimental philosophy is rejected in principle. His experiments with magnets [5] are called a waste of time, and his fundamental discoveries in electricity and magnetism which have proved basic are characterized as fables.[6]

3. Not only did Bacon ignore or oppose what was sound in the science of his day, but he himself, despite all his grandiloquent claims, failed to make a single important contribution to science.

The only two claims in this respect that I have ever seen are that Bacon anticipated Newton's discovery of gravitation and that he discovered heat to be a form of motion. Neither of these claims is true.

The first claim is made by Voltaire in the famous essay which did more than anything else to establish Bacon's great European reputation. But the claim that Bacon anticipated Newton's law of gravitation is absurd on the face of it, since the Newtonian theory is based on the Copernican astronomy, which Bacon rejected. Moreover, Voltaire, like other admirers of Bacon, does not seem to have read Bacon with care or noticed his distinct assertion that bodies lose weight below the surface of the earth.[7] Newton could certainly not have been influenced by such nonsense. Bacon's knowledge that the speed of falling bodies increases as they approach the earth—which Voltaire confuses with the law of gravitation —was an old commonplace in no way discovered by Bacon,

[4] *Ibid.*, I, 66.
[5] *Ibid.*, I, 70.

[6] *Ibid.*, II, 48.
[7] *Ibid.*, I, 33.

whose views went no deeper than the observation that some bodies are heavy, some light, and some neither.[8]

The second claim, that Bacon anticipated the modern doctrine of heat as a form of motion, is likewise untenable. For Bacon rejected the atomic theory (*Novum Organum,* II, 8), and his method of induction led him to infer that the motion which produces heat "should take place not in the very minutest particles but rather in those of some tolerable dimensions." [9]

How far Bacon himself was from making any fruitful contributions to science is amply illustrated by the observations and conclusions on almost every page of his *Sylva Sylvarum* and other pretended scientific works. A few examples from the more widely read *Novum Organum* may be cited: Refusing to grant that fire can ever separate the elements of a compound, he recommends the study of the spirit in every body, "whether that spirit is copious and exuberant, or meager and scarce, fine or coarse, aeriform or igniform, etc." [10] Or consider the queer jumble of unrelated phenomena in his tables of instances on which an induction as to heat is to be based, containing the following gems: Confined air is particularly warm in winter, and "the irritation of surrounding cold increases heat as may be seen in fires during a sharp frost." All shaggy substances are warm, and so are spirits of wine. Boiling water surpasses in heat some flames, etc. I am not unaware that with due diligence somewhat similar absurdities may be culled from the pages of Gilbert, Kepler, Galileo, Boyle, and even later writers in the Transactions of the Royal Society. But these men have positive achievement in science to their credit. Bacon has none. Nor could he very well have made any scientific discoveries so long as he believed in explaining things by "spirits" and relying on "axioms" whereby "gold or any metal or stone is generated from the original menstruum." [11]

[8] Top. Part Sc. Ob. 3.
[9] *Novum Organum,* II, 20.
[10] *Ibid.,* II, 7.
[11] *Ibid.,* II, 5.

4. Others have urged that while Bacon did not himself make any direct contribution to science, he founded the true method of science, the method of induction. There is, however, not a single authenticated record of anyone ever making any important discovery in science by following Bacon's method and its mechanical tables and twenty-seven prerogative instances. It would, indeed, be most amazing if the man who ignored or rejected what was soundest in the science of his day, and put down as fact or conclusion so many absurdities as Bacon did, should become the originator or true expounder of scientific method.

It is true that some scientists, e.g., Boyle and other founders of the Royal Society, paid great tribute to Bacon. But none of their really scientific contributions was determined by the Baconian method. It was rather the methods which Bacon rejected, the methods of Kepler, Galileo, and Gilbert, that they followed in their successful efforts. Also, the idea of a society for the promotion of natural and experimental knowledge was developed by the Italians (e.g., the Lincean Society, of which Galileo was a member) long before Bacon.

We need not ignore the fact that in the first book of the *Novum Organum* and more especially in his doctrine of the idols, Bacon has given us a most vivid, stirring and still applicable account of the perennial difficulties in the scientific study of nature. But his unusually eloquent appeal for the study of facts as opposed to idle speculation was neither new nor in fact very effective in the actual development of science. In the century before Bacon the Spaniard Vives had made the same criticisms, the same exhortations and almost the same grandiose plans. Indeed, we find the same appeal for the direct study of nature continually urged as far back as the twelfth century by the scholastic Adelard of Bath. But it is all rather futile. Science flourishes not on good intentions produced by pious exhortations, but on the suggestion of definite directions of inquiry and definite workable methods, and these Bacon entirely failed to produce.

Bacon's failure is most instructive because it shows the illusory character of the idea of induction which he and Mill after him made popular. According to this view the scientist begins without any regard for previous thought. Resolved not to anticipate nature, he lets the facts record their own tale. All this is purely Utopian. The facts of nature do not stream in on us with all their relevant characteristics duly marked. The number of possible circumstances that can be noted about any object is indefinitely large. Scientific progress depends upon considering only the circumstances that turn out to be relevant to the point of our inquiry. But what we consider relevant, e.g., in the inquiry as to the cause of cancer, depends upon previous knowledge. Hence scientific discoveries are not made by those who begin with an unbiased mind in the form of a *tabula rasa,* but by those who have derived fruitful ideas from the study of previous science. In the absence of carefully considered methods of observation that depend upon previous knowledge and critical reflection, the observation of nature herself is sterile. Those who think they can start any natural inquiry without "anticipating nature" or making any assumptions at all are just complacently ignorant. In any case, anyone who begins, in the Baconian fashion, to observe nature *de novo* is bound to find many "facts" which are not so. Thus Bacon himself observes that cold diminishes after passing a certain altitude,[12] that air is transformed into water,[13] that water in wells is warmer in winter than in summer,[14] and that the moon draws forth heat, induces putrefaction, increases moisture and excites the motions of spirits.[15] Of course many of the absurd observations that crowd the pages of Bacon were made for him by some of his assistants, like the Reverend Rawley, or taken from popular manuals of his day. But they are in any case typical of what untrained observers can and do record. No reader of Bacon can question his genius or the fertility of his

[12] *Novum Organum,* II, 27.   [14] *Ibid.,* 885.
[13] *Sylva Sylvarum,* 27.   [15] *Ibid.,* 889.

mind; but a comparison of his ideas on science with the works of previous scientists upon whom he heaped rhetorical scorn shows the utter irrelevance of Bacon's ideas to the actual progress of science. Thus his classification of the types of motion displays great ingenuity. But all such concepts as the "motion of liberty," in which bodies "strive with all their power to rebound and resume their former density," lack the direct relevance which we find in the ideas of the sixteenth-century Italian predecessors of Galileo, like Benedetti. Compare similarly Bacon's vague statements about colors as "solitary" instances or white color as a "migratory" instance with the observations of Kepler's *Dioptrics* or even with the observations on the rainbow in Vitello's *Optics* published in 1270. The utter futility of the untrained amateur in science is borne in on us when we compare Bacon's ideas on the motion of the pulse, or his explanation of sex organs [16] with the contemporary work of Harvey.

No wonder that a real scientist like Harvey was moved to say that Bacon wrote science like a lord chancellor.

How, then, in the light of the foregoing readily verifiable facts, are we to explain the tremendous extent and persistence of the tradition that looks to Bacon as the founder of modern science?

The first point to note is that Bacon is still eminently readable, while the scientific works of Kepler, Galileo, Gilbert, and Harvey, not to mention their predecessors, are inaccessible to the general reader. The change from Latin to the vernacular as the language of the learned, together with the rapid growth of new technical methods since the eighteenth century, has made it difficult for scientists themselves to read the works of their predecessors of the sixteenth or previous centuries. But Bacon can be read by everybody. His pithy sayings are sententious and quotable like Cicero's. The general reader is carried away by the splendid rhetoric with which Bacon

[16] *Novum Organum*, I, 27.

denounces as useless all previous work in science; and his errors of fact or irrelevance of ideas are either not recognized as such or else covered by the very broad but unhistorical reflection that they were good enough for Bacon's times.

The main source, however, of the Baconian myth is the great romantic appeal which inheres in the fundamental idea of organizing science on a new basis calling for no special aptitude or technical training. Technical science involves an arduous routine which cannot be popular with the uninitiated. The multitude (including scientists away from their special domain) will always delight in any plan for a new deal in science—"a discovery which will lead to the discovery of everything else," [17] or "a synopsis of all the natures that exist in the universe." [18] That which makes utopias spring up perennially is found in Bacon's idea that if his system could be established "the invention of all causes and sciences would be the labor of but a few years." [19] Especially in an age that believes in democracy and mechanical progress it is pleasant to be told that science exists for material enrichment and that everything can be achieved by rules leaving little to superior wits.[20] It requires painful efforts to disabuse ourselves of such pleasant illusion.

[17] *Novum Organum*, I, 129.
[18] *Ibid.*, II, 21.
[19] *Ibid.*, I, 112.
[20] *Ibid.*, I, 111, and I, 122.

BOOK TWO

PHILOSOPHICAL REFLECTIONS

THE NEW REALISM

I

THOUGH THE POLEMIC SPIRIT has for some time filled the air of philosophy, the numerous marches and counter-marches cannot be said to have proved decisive. As the walls of philosophy refuse to fall at the mere flourish of trumpets, there has been little change in the *status quo*. Everyone interested in genuine philosophic progress will therefore welcome this volume [1] and its well-organized attempt to advance the position outlined in the "Platform." [2] Unless I am very much mistaken, however, the authors of this book may be—pleasantly or unpleasantly—surprised at being welcomed by many idealists, who will regard them, not as hostile invaders, but as much-needed immigrants taking possession of the abandoned or undeveloped soil and rendering it fruitful for the common good. Perhaps the authors of this book may resent this attempt to minimize the importance of the destructive mission of their "class consciousness," but I think philosophers generally are more fortunate in delivering the positive burden of their own vision than in their denial of the vision of others. The polemic consciousness is not in any of its forms conducive to complete justice, and history is full of examples of philosophers, like Aristotle, attacking most vehemently those most closely related to them. It is indeed a wise philosopher who knows his own true opponent. Now neo-realism looks upon idealism [3] as the great enemy, because as a matter of fact the

[1] Edwin B. Holt, Walter T. Marvin, William Pepperell Montague, Ralph Barton Perry, Walter B. Pitkin, and Edward Gleason Spaulding, *The New Realism: Cooperative Studies in Philosophy* (Macmillan Company, New York, 1912).

[2] *The Journal of Philosophy*, Vol. VII, pp. 393 ff.

[3] The essence of idealism, as that term has been used in philosophy, literature, art, politics, etc., is that the structure of the universe justifies certain values, called ideals, and with that doctrine the authors of this

former movement originated in a reaction against such types of idealism as are embodied in Bradley's *Appearance and Reality* and Strong's *Why the Mind Has a Body*. When, however, one disregards the accidental starting point and judges neo-realism by its fundamental tendency, the opposition between realism and dualistic or psychologic pragmatism will be seen to be of far greater significance. Between a position which would regard everything in terms of the subject and a position which would regard everything as objective, there may be very little or no *theoretic* difference, for the same laws or relations may hold between "experiences" as between "independent reals," i.e., the distinction between different classes of entities may be the same in the two systems. Between a view, however, which insists that the propositions of logic and mathematics are as real or objective (i.e., independent of "mind") as those of physics, and a view which denies to objects of thought the ontologic status of objects of sense, the issue is significant, and, it seems to me, laden with momentous consequences. I regard, therefore, the problem of the reality of universals, "the things of thought," as the central question which this volume raises. It is not, then, so much Berkeley's subjectivism (about which there is considerable doubt) as his nominalism that presents the significant alternative to the neo-realist position. At any rate, if Professor Marvin's paper proves its point, the epistemologic issue cannot be the fundamental one, but must yield in fundamental importance to issues of fact or theories of being.

Nominalism, the denial of "reality" to relations, abstractions, etc., is based on the conscious or unconscious assump-

book have no quarrel whatsoever. They are fighting epistemologic subjectivism; but for some unaccountable reason they always call it idealism. That this use of the word "idealism" involves unusual violence to the facts of history, e.g., in the implication that an idealist like Hegel is an epistemologic subjectivist, ought to be clear to all students of the history of philosophy. But this is a minor matter, if the sympathetic reader will simply substitute the word *subjectivism* wherever the authors use the word *idealism*.

tion of the ancient dogma that only a whole can really exist and that which is a part (in intension) cannot have independent existence. The essence of neo-realism, the object's independence of our apprehension of it, as developed by Professor Perry, would be utterly impossible on a nominalistic metaphysic, and so would Professor Spaulding's doctrine of analytic realism. At any rate, it is a significant fact that the one positive doctrine which all the six authors find themselves compelled to use in their arguments, is the nonmental character of the propositions of logic and mathematics.[4]

There is, to be sure, a certain hesitation in the authors' repudiation of nominalism (e.g., p. 58).[5] While in general they "accord full ontological status to things of thought," logical and mathematical entities are denied the claim to existence, but are put in the undefined but spacious realm of subsistence. I cannot, however, but regard the distinction between existence and subsistence—which the authors have borrowed from Russell—as merely a temporary or provisional makeshift. Certain sensible or physical terms in time and space are regarded as existents, and all other possible or impossible objects of thought are subsistents. This, like most dichotomous divisions, can hardly be expected to be of much use; for it puts too many things in the negative class (in this case, the class of subsistents). The question is important, because the facile division of objects into existent and subsistent tends to obscure the fundamental problem or requirement of any constructive philosophy, viz., a systematic classification of reals, or a doctrine of categories. To the neglect of this problem may be ascribed a great deal of the misunderstanding and futility of modern philosophic controversy.

The distinction between existence and subsistence arises from a certain requirement in the modern philosophy of mathematics, viz., that mathematical propositions shall have

---

[4] Marvin, pp. 57 ff., Perry, pp. 129 ff., Spaulding, pp. 204-205, Montague, pp. 261-262, Holt, pp. 363 ff. and p. 472, Pitkin, pp. 445 ff.

[5] The word nominalism does not occur in the index.

a meaning which is nonpsychologic and nonphysical. Russell expresses this fact by saying that mathematical entities must be nonmental and nonexistential. Hence the term subsistence to cover those entities. The restriction, however, of the term existence to sensible objects, which this terminology implies, leads to considerable confusion in the neo-realist philosophy.[6] Russell's statement, repeated by Marvin (p. 85), that the nonexistential character of mathematics is one of the greatest discoveries of the nineteenth century, is, of course, true. But what it means is simply that mathematical propositions are formal, and their truth is independent of the truths of physics. Mathematical entities, then, are not physical, but they certainly have being as much as physical entities do. What reason can there be, outside of a nominalistic metaphysic, for denying the existence of one and not of the other? Moreover, the restriction of the existential predicate to sensible terms gives rise to confusion in the realm where the distinction between existence and subsistence first arose, viz., mathematics. When a mathematician proves an existence theorem, e.g., that every equation of the nth degree has n roots, he surely establishes something more than the subsistence of these n roots, for the $n + 1$th root of the same equation has according to the canon of the neo-realists (Montague, p. 253) subsistence though demonstrably no existence. The difficulty here raised does not seem to be sufficiently met by Russell's contention that mathematical existence denotes something totally (i.e., generically) different from physical existence. For, if mathematical existence is only a kind of subsistence, it is surely of the utmost

[6] Russell says: "Except space and time themselves, only those objects exist which have to particular points of space and time the special relation of occupying them" (*Mind* [1904], p. 211). I take it that Russell means to predicate existence of those things only which occupy *both* time and space; so that things occupying time only, e.g., misunderstandings of realism, do not exist. Moreover, in the light of other utterances, Russell probably means that only points of space and time exist, but that the series denoted by the terms time and space, like existence itself, do not exist.

importance to distinguish between the subsistence of the nth root and the subsistence of the $n + 1$th root. Instead, then, of inquiring into the kinds of existence, we have to inquire into the kinds or grades of subsistence.

Is it true, however, that mathematical and physical existences are so generically different that they have nothing in common? For one thing the determination of physical existence is frequently, if not always, based on mathematical existence. Moreover, the manner in which mathematical and physical existences are determined is exactly the same. Take the questions: Is there a root to every equation? Is there a maximum velocity in the physical universe? Is there a special sex-determining factor in the germ cell? Did Moses have a real (historical) existence? Now in all these significant questions, the existence or nonexistence of the entities in question is determined, in their respective sciences, not by reference to the question whether they are mental, but by reference to their relation to the body of propositions which form the sciences in question.[7] What reason can there be, on realistic ground, for saying that roots and velocities have no existence, but that the other entities do? Does it not seem that what we need is a fuller account of the different levels or types of existence?

This question of the distinction between existence and subsistence is an illustration of the truth of the authors' contention (pp. 21-22) that care in the use of words is really important. An adequate doctrine of categories would do away with a great many of the difficulties which Montague, for instance, finds in the existence of error and hallucinatory objects. (This does not hold of Holt's theory.) Errors and false propositions do undoubtedly exist in this world, if anything does. The significant question is how do they exist, i.e., to what type of existence do they belong. Many people, for instance, will find unconvincing Spaulding's arguments for the

---

[7] This point is missed by most critics of realism, e.g., Professor Pratt, *The Journal of Philosophy*, Vol. IX, p. 579.

existence of points in space, or of atoms in material bodies, and will find good reasons for their unbelief. This situation arises from the fact that points are nonspatial (i.e., nonextended) and atoms nonmaterial (i.e., devoid of the ordinary properties of matter). Points and atoms, then, do not have the *kind* of existence of space and matter; and unless this distinction is clearly recognized, both the affirmative and the negative positions seem equally tenable or untenable.

In the light of a developed doctrine of categories, also, the distinction between discovery and invention, between finding and making, which dominates neo-realism in its present stage, may turn out not to be as thoroughgoing as it appears in the light of current controversy. The distinction in question is certainly valid for a great many types of reality. There is a real logical opposition between discovering and inventing a polar continent. But did the Romans invent or discover their jurisprudence? Did the authors of this book invent or discover the neo-realist philosophy? These questions suggest the possibility of a realm where invention and discovery overlap, or cease to be clearly antithetic terms.

The authors' own statement (pp. 2-10) of the historical significance of neo-realism seems rather unfortunate. The account in question reads too much like an Hegelian *a priori* history, with its distinct stages each by a dialectic process giving rise to its successor. I regard it as unfortunate because it is not likely to discourage critics from dealing with neo-realism as a new epistemology, whereas it is really a return to a mode of thought in which the epistemologic specter need not trouble us. Take, for instance, the theory of error. The authors (and their critics, like Professor Lovejoy) assume that the first method of explaining error is by the introduction of mind or consciousness. That, however, is not the fact, for this action of consciousness as a disturbing medium seems to have been suggested by the modern use of lenses. The earlier attempt to explain error, found alike among the Hindoos and Greek philosophers, is to give error a kind of secondary or shadowy existence of its own. *Maya* is not due merely to consciousness, but is a sort of maze or fog which surrounds the real, and "the way of error" in Parmenides is certainly not "the way of consciousness." The neo-realist doctrine of error (as briefly indicated in the essays of Holt and Pitkin) will, in fact, be found to begin where the Greeks left off, and to develop the ancient method in a form consonant with the requirements of modern science.

The one modern movement with which neo-realism *is* closely allied (in motive, at least), is radical empiricism. James was profoundly dissatisfied with the prevailing nominalism, and saw that it must logically lead to a hopeless and lifeless atomism. James tried to restore in philosophy the fluency of things, by giving relations, transitions, etc., a psychologic status. Neo-realism aims at the same results, but turns its back on any attempt to construct the world out of psychologic states. In the light of modern mathematical research, it returns to the Aristotelian insight that what is prior in knowledge need not be prior in nature, and thus reopens the path of progress along which all the objective sciences have been going, but which has been shut to philosophy by the specters of epistemology.

II

THE LOGICAL and historical introduction to neo-realism is to be found in Professor Marvin's essay on "The Emancipation of Metaphysics from Epistemology." The neo-realist movement is a "reaction against the whole enterprise of Locke, Kant, and their followers, to get a fundamental science, and not merely against their idealism. Neo-realism is not only a different theory of knowledge, but what is more important for metaphysics, a different doctrine as to the place of epistemology in the hierarchy of the sciences" (p. 51). Professor Marvin does well to refer thus to Locke as the father of criticism, for Kant's boastful claim often makes us forget that it was

Locke who first set in fashion the view that we must examine the nature of knowledge before "we let loose our thoughts into the vast ocean of being." [8] Professor Marvin's attack, however, is directed more particularly against the Kantian view of an *a priori* science of knowledge as the necessary prerequisite for metaphysics. To offset criticism by the mere use of epithets, Professor Marvin adopts the admirable device of calling his position "dogmatism" and opposing it to "criticism." Kant's assumption of the possibility of a science or "critique" which can determine *a priori* the nature, possibility, and limits of knowledge, is really untenable; for epistemology can function only if it assumes that we already are in possession of valid knowledge, and this knowledge, as a matter of fact, it borrows from logic, psychology, etc. The "possibility" of mathematics, physics, or metaphysics is far less questionable than the possibility of epistemology. The neo-Kantian may reply: "Of course we must assume that we are in possession of valid knowledge in order to proceed at all. But Kant never supposes that the validity of science is in need of proof. The significant question for him is, What are the conditions which make valid knowledge possible?" To which we may answer, that this way of putting the question is inconsistent with the claim of epistemology as an *a priori* science more fundamental than metaphysics or psychology, for the actual conditions of valid knowledge can be determined only on the basis of logical, psychological, or metaphysical data. Indeed, Kant himself really does assume a particular system of psychology of various "faculties," and certain definite views of reality, in order to work out his deductions of the categories and other parts of his critique of pure reason. This Kantian metaphysics may be valid. What Professor Marvin is intent on proving is that it does not follow from, but, on the contrary, is the basis of Kant's epistemology. The same may be said of the neo-Hegelian metaphysics of Greene and his followers,

[8] Essay I, Ch. I, Sec. 7.

which they claim rests on an examination of the nature of knowledge. The history of science shows no important scientific advance or metaphysical progress due to epistemology. On the contrary, whatever influence the latter has exerted on the former seems to have been pernicious. The various sciences and metaphysics, therefore, are and by right ought to be, free and independent of the sovereignty of epistemology, and they may go on to develop their fields without waiting for the issue of a permit by the science of epistemology.

This, I take it, is the gist of Professor Marvin's careful and most conscientiously worked out argument. It seems so cogent and unanswerable that it arouses a very distressing reflection: Why has philosophy so long failed to note this? Marvin's argument has been, in part at least, made by such different writers as Hegel [9] and the Friesian school,[10] but the intellectual world, without stopping to refute these arguments, has calmly ignored them. Even the positive sciences now feel it incumbent upon them to pay their respects to *Erkenntnistheorie,* while metaphysics is considered as belonging to the intellectual underworld. Nay, even Professor Marvin himself subscribes to the statement of his colleagues that the epistemologic question "is prior to all other philosophic issues" (p. 10).

Perhaps, however, the line between neo-realism and criticism is not as sharp as Professor Marvin draws it. What Kant calls transcendental method is not very much different in essence from that which Marvin calls logical analysis and which, he maintains, is independent of psychology. The more fundamental difference, I venture to think, lies elsewhere, viz., in the conception of the realm of metaphysics. Kant's metaphysic is essentially antievolutionary, *a priori,* and incapable of progress. "Pure speculative reason," he tells us, "is able to give a complete enumeration of the possible modes of proposing problems to itself, and thus sketch out the entire system

[9] *Encyklopädie,* Sec. 41.
[10] L. Nelson, *Über das sogenannte Erkenntnisproblem.*

of metaphysics"; and again, metaphysics, by means of criticism, "can take in the whole sphere of its cognitions, and can thus complete its work, and leave it for the use of posterity, as a capital which can never receive fresh accessions." [11] If we no longer believe reality to be such a closed and limited system, then we must give up the attempt to deduce it *a priori* and complete from the nature of knowledge as such.

This antievolutionary view in the background of criticism explains why the most blighting effects of criticism have been felt by such young growing sciences as sociology and jurisprudence.[12] Workers in these fields are distracted at the outset by purely formal problems, as what is the nature of social science, its method, its object, its limits, etc., etc. But there is no way of finding the limits of science except by actually developing it first. Epistemologic criticism is applicable to science only when the latter is in a state of *relative* completion, e.g., in certain fields of mathematics and physics. Then questions of procedure, the convenience of hypotheses, etc., have a definite meaning. But such considerations must follow and cannot precede the constructive stage.

The elimination of "critical" epistemology leaves the field clear for constructive metaphysics. Now, unlike most recent philosophic procedures, neo-realism takes modern physical science seriously, or, if you please, naïvely. It does not regard it as a "mere construction of the mind," a more or less useful falsehood, but as a valid method of discovering the constitution of reality. Hence, in adopting the mathematical or analytic method of science as also valid for philosophy, neo-realism finds itself under the guns of men like Bradley and Bergson, who deny that analysis can enable us to reach ultimate reality, and insist that it must necessarily falsify the real. Hence the need for Spaulding's essay, "A Defence of Analysis," "as a method of knowing which discovers entities or parts

[11] Preface to 2d ed., *Kritik der reinen Vernunft*, p. xxiii.
[12] See Cosentini, in *Revue Int. de Sociologie*, Jan., 1913; and Fragpane, *Obbietto e limite della filosofia del diritto*, II, pp. 77-83.

which are real in quite the same sense as are the wholes which are analyzed" (p. 155). The neo-realist is quite willing to admit that the actual analyses which men make are selected from a larger number of possible ones, but this does not prove that they are falsifications. If there are more parts or further divisions than those employed in our analysis, it does not follow that our analysis is false: it may be true as far as it goes. As the opponents of analysis do themselves employ analysis in their attempt to prove their contention, it is at least doubtful whether *all* analysis can be false *qua* analysis. Professor Spaulding, therefore, examines in detail the various types of analysis, viz., that of aggregates, classes, and organic unities, and shows that in each case the objections are invalid.

An aggregate is analyzed by enumeration, i.e., by naming the parts and the conjunctive relation. Why is this falsification? Because, says Bergson, there is no genuine plurality in nature itself, but all things interpenetrate.[13] This assumption, however, of a *universal* interpenetration is a mere snap judgment or violent generalization without adequate evidence. Any evidence for interaction must, of course, begin by recognizing different things which interact.

Under the analysis of classes Spaulding includes the analysis of number, space, time, motion, velocity, and acceleration, and such classes of individuals as atoms, electrons, etc. The attack on this kind of analysis is stated by Bergson in a form the logic of which is identical with that of Zeno's attack on motion. According to this attack analysis breaks up space into non-extended points, time into unenduring moments, and motion into a series of rests. But these supposed parts are the contradictions of the given wholes. Therefore analysis is falsification. To which Professor Spaulding justly replies that this attack ignores and misstates the actual results of modern analysis. The divisibility of continuous space does not lead to discreteness, but, on the contrary, defines definitely what

---

[13] *Creative Evolution,* pp. 11, 162, 188, 338, 340.

is meant by continuity; and, in the same way, it is not true that modern analysis resolves motion into a series of rests. In its account of analysis, this attack leaves out the *organizing relations*. While points, for example, are nonextended, there is no contradiction in saying that space is a class of points between which certain relations hold. "Consider both terms *and* relations and the properties of the whole which may be left over, but which are revealed by analysis, and the analysis becomes *adequate* at the same time that there is opportunity for that 'creative evolution,' for that creative synthesis which some of the attacking party emphasize so strongly, but which is not dependent, for its acceptance, upon the validity of the attack" (p. 168).

Organic unities are distinguished by the fact that they are wholes possessing properties which are not the sum of the properties of the parts. This, however, is not confined, as is usually supposed, to organisms. There are *some* qualities in a compound like water which cannot be obtained by adding the qualities of the components. But whether the parts modify each other when united, or whether new organizing relations arise when the parts are united as they were not before, in either case scientific analysis or synthesis is adequate to reveal the real change in nature. The introduction of entelechies to distinguish organisms from inorganic physico-chemical complexes is either scientifically pernicious or unnecessary, according to whether the entelechies do or do not introduce an element of indeterminism. A supervening awareness may occur, and "it is good realism to admit that it may," but it cannot be used as a principle of explanation.

The attack on conceptual analysis as conceptismal, is based on the argument that concepts are necessarily static and inadequate to grasp change or process. But why assume that only like entities can be related? The concept of divisibility need not be divisible. At any rate, there is no real contradiction in a definite or fixed concept of a flow, and Bergson himself uses concepts to denote the three *kinds* of change

In this connection Professor Spaulding briefly indicates (p. 233) four important characteristics of concepts, or "states of affairs." These will well bear more extensive development in a future paper.

It must be conceded, I think, that Professor Spaulding's very laboring arguments show the utter flimsiness of the attack on analysis, so far as the latter is based on the argument that analysis of space, time, or motion leads to contradiction. This last argument simply ignores the fact that modern mathematics, by its analysis of infinity and continuity, has definitely solved Zeno's puzzles. Besides, the charge of contradiction comes with bad grace from those who are skeptical about the force of logical contradiction when it is applied to their own doctrines. Nevertheless, there is an element of real force in the contention that analysis is by itself inadequate to give us a complete account of space, time, and motion, and that resort to intuition is necessary. Mathematical analysis can reveal to us only the formal or structural properties of such entities as space. Having started with a number of postulates relating to indefinable "points," the properties deduced will be the same if these "points" are numbers, ideal citizens of an ideal commonwealth, or what not, so long as the defining relations hold between them. What distinguishes physical space from any other possible interpretation of S (mathematical space) can, therefore, be grasped only by intuition. Spaulding's statement (following Russell) that "points" are spatial is hardly warranted by his own analysis, in which "points" are necessarily (not "probably") indefinable. Professor Spaulding also seems to forget that space is not determined solely as a point collection; it may also be constituted in diverse other ways, e.g., as a four-dimensional collection of lines, in which the lines are the simple elements and points are complexes formed by the intersection of lines. This, of course, in no way militates against the validity of any of these analyses of space. The same thing may be correctly expressed in different sets of units without damage to realism. But reflection on these considerations enables one to understand some of the *motives* of those to whom the world appears more fluid than to Professor Spaulding. Indeed, there is a hard and fast finality about some of the latter's statements which is hardly warranted by the present state of science, e.g., the statement that points presuppose numbers (p. 174) is certainly not true if we restrict ourselves to projective geometry. In his realistic zeal, also, Professor Spaulding seems to me to obliterate the distinction between hypothesis and fact, as in his argument for the reality of indivisible atoms. It is well to take science seriously, but why should philosophers be compelled to take scientific hypotheses more seriously than scientists themselves do? Why pin the hope of our salvation on indivisible atoms when leading chemists like Ostwald, Duhem, and others can get along without them? Moreover, many scientists who profess their allegiance to the atomic hypothesis do so merely as a matter of form. Take any textbook on crystallography, on the phase rule, or on any branch of thermodynamics, and you may find a good deal said at the beginning about the atomic constitution of matter; but when the real work begins all that is silently disregarded, and integration formulae are introduced which presuppose the continuity of matter. Indeed, the attitude of most working scientists today to the atomic and other regnant theories is very much like that of the Mexican governor who is reported to have said: "I owe allegiance to whatever brigand is duly elected president, but first of all I must maintain order in my own province." Whatever objections may be brought against this view, it at least saves us from the extremes of anarchy and vicious absolutism.

Professor Perry's essay, "A Realistic Theory of Independence," is a painstaking attempt to define the distinctive epistemologic doctrine of neo-realism. The new realism differs from the old realism of Reid in giving up the doctrine of a substance behind the qualities. (I am not sure whether Professor Montague always does so.) Its distinctive note is that the object is independent of the knower. What does this mean? It does not mean, we are told, the absence of any relation between the object and our knowledge, nor does the neo-realist even wish to deny that knowledge may be in some sense prior to the object. By the term independent we are to understand simply the absence of certain specific relations which constitute dependence. "In order to prove the dependence of *a* on *b* it is necessary to show that *a* contains *b*; or that *a* is the cause or effect of *b* in a system which exclusively determines *a*; or that *a* implies *b*; or that *a* is implied exclusively by *b*. To exhibit any relation of *a* to *b* other than these is beside the point. Whether *a* and *b* be otherwise related, or not, does not affect the independence of *a*" (p. 117).

It is clear that with this definition of dependence our opponent will never be able to prove the dependence of the object on consciousness; for, if it can be shown that the object is in any way determined by something else, it can no longer be said to be exclusively determined by consciousness and is, therefore, independent. On the other hand, so far as this definition goes, one may believe that consciousness modifies every real and yet maintain that the latter is independent of the former—which would make it seem as if the chief novelty of neo-realism on this point is the use of the word *independent* in an unusual sense. Indeed, the proposed definition of independence is not only somewhat unusual, but even directly contrary to popular use which conceives what is included, implied, caused, or explained as the dependent term rather than that which contains, implies, causes, or explains (p. 115). Certainly a use of the term *dependence* which makes the premises of a syllogism depend on the conclusion (p. 121) involves some violence to ordinary usage. The neo-realist, of course, has a perfect right to define his terms in any way he pleases; but as he cannot change the flavor which words carry along with them, some confusion is bound to result.

The really vital point of Professor Perry's argument, however, consists in the elimination of the egocentric predicament, by showing that the ubiquity of the knowledge relation is irrelevant in the determination of the real. Indeed, scientific procedure depends on this very ability to show that a condition may be irrelevant even though it is always present. "It is the task of science to distinguish within a total manifold those factors which do count and those which do not." Thus, e.g., the equality of the ratios between the sides of a triangle and the sines of the opposite angles is discovered in a larger context containing, among other things, the absolute magnitude of the sides; but though present, the absolute magnitude does not count. Similarly, "when Galileo discovered that acceleration was a function of the time of a body's fall, he discovered that it was not a function of the body's weight or volume. And to establish this it was not necessary for him to obtain an instance of a body without weight or volume; it was sufficient for him to show that the factors, although present, *did not enter into the calculation*" (p. 132). From this it clearly follows that an object *may* enter into or go out of the cognitive situation without losing its independence.

In the concluding portion of this essay, Professor Perry examines various cases of "subjectivity," and concludes that the whole realm of value, art, history, society, life, etc., is dependent on consciousness, though independent of reflective or secondary conscious relations with which it may enter. This admission or qualification may minimize the issue between realism and "idealism"; but the critical onlooker may well ask whether it does not prejudice the argument in the earlier portion of the essay. Where is the difference in point of objectivity or independence between a proposition of mathematics and one of economics? Many judgments of value are purely logical or mathematical. The test is laid down that "in so far as any given object is deducible otherwise than from consciousness, it is independent of consciousness" (p. 135); and from this it is argued that if the mean velocity of Jupiter can be deduced from the gravitational system without reference to cognition it must be considered independent of the latter. But is not the economic value of a thing in the same way determined, not by reference to cognition, but by its quality, quantity, cost of production, etc.?

It would be a pity if Professor Perry's view, that judgments of value have not the same objectivity as judgments of mathematics or logic, were to lead to the view that neo-realism has no message for ethics or philosophy of life. To at least one reader of this volume the great promise of neo-realism is precisely in the latter direction. The great confusion and futility of social theory today seems to me to result from the attempt to build up a social philosophy on a nominalistic logic. Nominalistic logic must inevitably lead to atomistic individualism and to a psychology of moments or "states," as can be seen in the history of ethics from Antisthenes to Bentham or Spencer. By emphasizing the reality of universals or "organizing relations," by recognizing the latter as real causes, neo-realism supplies a much-needed aid to the analysis of the larger life.

Professor Perry and his colleagues frequently speak of absolute simples. It is worth while raising the issue whether there are such things. The argument is advanced that analysis, i.e., the recognition of complexes, presupposes the existence of simples. But obviously this simplicity is always relative to a specific complex. In another context this simple term may itself be very complex. Smith may be a simple unit for purposes of vital statistics, but infinitely complex to his teacher, business partner, or sweetheart. A point is a simple entity in our ordinary three-dimensional space, but a complex in line geometry; and so atoms, electrons, the color green, etc., are simples in certain contexts and complex in others. Even logical ideas like "implication," "disjunction," "negation," etc., can be simple ideas in one system, and complex in another. (Compare the indefinables of Russell's *Principles of Mathematics* with those of the *Principia Mathematica*.)

The foregoing three essays may be considered as an attempt to clear the ground and indicate the method for a constructive metaphysic. Thus considered they represent the necessary common ground for the six writers. The remaining three essays are devoted to a special problem which arises on this common ground, viz., the nature of consciousness and error. As the solutions which Professors Montague, Holt, and Pitkin offer differ from each other, and as in the present temper of philosophic discussion this topic is certain to receive more than its due share of attention, it is not necessary to review it here in detail.

In his suggestive essay, "A Realistic Theory of Truth and Error," Professor Montague approaches the problem from a modified form of his theory which identifies consciousness with potential energy. Consciousness consists of the self-transcending implications which the brain-states sustain to their extraorganic causes (or effects). "Now if we single out some one event and inquire as to its cause, we shall find a plurality of possible antecedents, any one of which if it had not been counteracted would have produced it. . . . It follows from this that the implicate or conscious object of any brain state may be, but need not be, an event which actually exists" (p. 287). According, then, as the implicates are real things or their contradictories we have truth or error.

The anthropomorphic or "common sense" view of causality which this theory involves is of such limited application that Professor Montague is sure to encounter considerable trouble in convincing others of its adequacy. Professor Pitkin, for one, is convinced that implication or meaning is of much wider extent than causality, e.g., the triangle implies (in Euclidean space) a constant sum of interior angles; but the angles are neither the cause nor the effect of the triangle (p. 485). It seems as if Professor Montague, the pioneer of neo-realism in this country, is in danger of being considered a reactionary by his more progressive or radical brethren. Thus, he refuses to accept the relational formula which would explain the real existence of an optically bent but tactually straight stick. He does not allow hallucinatory objects to invade the "real" world, and lapses into such traditional utterances as "my awareness of objects is more certainly real than anything else" (p. 269), and "we are more certain of our own thoughts and feelings than of anything else" (p. 290). In spite of the fact that he clearly points out that it is not because of any character of belief, but "because of what is believed that the belief is true or false," he is not willing to accept the view that truth or falsehood are qualities of certain objects or complexes.

In common with Professor Spaulding and perhaps several other of his colleagues, Professor Montague holds to the priority of empty time and space over the content which fills it. No proof is offered for this position, nor does it seem necessary for the realistic position. Realism does not seem inconsistent with the view that time is the measure of motion, and space a way of co-ordinating positions. Metaphysicians who assume an absolute time or space should at least reckon with the relativity theory of Einstein and Minkowski—the only theory which satisfactorily explains the Michaelson-Morley experiments. According to this theory the time interval is just as relative to the point of observation as the angle which a line subtends.

Anyone who is inclined to think that realism tends in the direction of materialism will find much food for thought in Professor Montague's keen criticisms of panhylism (pp. 269-272 and 277). Professor Pitkin in stating the agreement between Professors Montague, Holt, and himself says: "Whatever consciousness is, it is somehow connected with the activity of getting 'beyond space and time'; that is, of adjusting variously to events beyond the organism's own skin and to conditions more than material" (p. 485).

As original and constructive contributions to philosophy, quite apart from the realistic thesis, the essays of Professors Holt and Pitkin seem to me the most important in this volume. Professor Holt's remarkably well-organized attack on the theory of specific nerve energy cuts at the root of a good deal of the vain speculation which has overrun modern psychologic philosophy; and Professor Pitkin's effort at evolving a new system of categories wherewith to express our biologic experience will go far to remove the lighthearted reliance on the categories of popular biology which are frequently nothing but the remnants of outworn metaphysical systems. Limitations of space, however, and regard for the main current which runs through all the essays, make only scant treatment of them possible.

Some neo-realists and all their critics seem to feel that the problem of error is a crucial one for neo-realism. I confess that while the problem is one of the utmost importance, I cannot see that it is peculiarly a problem for the realist any more than for anybody else—and most modern schools have dodged it. If we maintain, as any analysis of scientific procedure compels us, that a proposition is true or false not because we make it or believe it, but because of what is asserted in it, or because of the relation it bears to other propositions, then it seems to follow that truth and falsehood are equally independent of the consciousness in which they appear. At any rate, there is no evidence from science that the line between the true and the false, the real and the erroneous, is identical with that between the nonmental and the mental. The denial of the realistic position, therefore, can be made only on the basis either that all objects are mental or that only unreal objects are of mental origin. The former does not explain the difference between the true and the false, and the latter admits the nonmental character of real objects.

Be that as it may, it is a fact that the existence of nonmental but illusory objects is generally considered paradoxical; and Professor Holt's essay, "The Place of Illusory Experience in a Realistic World," tries to meet the objections on this ground. The argument that in the case of an illusory object the person sees what is not there, hence the act of seeing is constitutive of the object, is met by showing many physical processes of copying, by cameras, etc., which reproduce the same distortions or reduplications of the objects concerned. There is, therefore, every reason to suppose that the distortion or reduplication is due not to consciousness, but to the physical relation between the sense organs and the object. Thus the relativity of secondary qualities, the production of negative or complementary after-images, etc., are paralleled by the action of thermometers, the receiving mast of a wireless telegraph system, etc. To the argument that the outside world contains only primary qualities and vibration rates, and that the secondary qualities must be aroused in the mind by specific nerve energies, Professor Holt, after thoroughly refuting the specific nerve-energy theory, produces a new hypothesis which attempts to deduce the secondary qualities from the frequency interval of nerve pulses or vibration, and thus reduce them to a genuine part of the objective order. As this hypothesis will probably be seen to greater advantage in his *The Concept of Consciousness,* discussion of it had better be postponed for the present. It is enough to indicate that it attempts to solve the problem of illusory objects by showing "that the nervous system, even when unstimulated from without, is able to generate within itself nerve currents of those frequencies whose density factor is the same as in ordinary peripheral stimulation (p. 352); hence the illusory object with its secondary qualities is a genuine part of the physical system.

The failure to work out clearly a theory of types or levels of existence gives the neo-realist assertion in regard to the *objectivity* of illusory objects the appearance of self-contradiction. It seems to say that these *illusory* or *unreal* objects are *true* or *real.*[14] The reader, however, must not interpret the argument that illusory objects are objective, nonmental, or parts of the physical world, to mean that they are true or existent reals, for the neo-realist does not believe that the objective is necessarily *existent;* it may merely have being or *subsistence.* Nor has the illusory object the quality of being

[14] It is so misunderstood by Professor McGilvary, *The Philosophical Review,* Vol. XXII, p. 64, line 8.

true. In the subsistent world all sorts of contradictory or opposite propositions are found side by side. It is only when we limit ourselves to "existent" entities that contradictory propositions can no longer be applicable (p. 366). (As thus used the term "existent" covers not only physical and mental terms, but also mathematical entities whose existence is demonstrated.)

Of great significance is Professor Holt's criticism of Mr. G. E. Moore's view that consciousness and its objects are distinct existents, between which there is only the unresolvable relation of awareness. The latter view seems to be based on an undue emphasis on the qualitative difference between the object and idea; thus, "fire burns, but the idea of fire does not," etc. Professor Holt's answer is, "Fire burns, but the shape of the flame does not." Surely the two are not, therefore, two distinct entities.

In his essay on "Some Realistic Implications of Biology," Professor Pitkin has attempted to introduce more material than can conveniently be compressed within the ninety pages at his disposal. It is to be hoped that he will soon expand this into a respectable volume and thus, perhaps, render it easier for the reader.

The main points which, as a result of his analysis of the biologic situation, he contributes to the realist position are:

1. The organism does not always modify the stimulus. As against Professor Dewey, for instance, it is maintained that "at least in some cases the eye activity does not condition the specific light-character of ether vibration, but only the distribution and employment of these" (p. 417).

2. The doctrine of internal relations and what is often called the "organic" view of things find no support from the facts of biology. According to the "organic" view every part of an organic whole depends upon the whole and no part can be removed without destroying the whole. The facts of experimental biology flatly disprove this so far as natural organisms are concerned.

3. Planes, angles, numbers, ratios, and other such mathematical-geometrical characters are genuine stimuli. They are thus real causes.

4. The cognitive situation can be interpreted realistically by means of a very suggestive analogy from projective geometry. Professor Pitkin thus tries to make clear "how errors, illusions, and hallucinations are not made by consciousness nor are peculiar to it, but are necessary features of a projected physical system" (p. 377).

Attempts like these to dispense with old accredited categories and to invent new descriptions which will eliminate discredited metaphysical doctrines, make neo-realism appear excessively technical and complex. However, if we distinguish between the familiar and the simple, may not such an attempt lead to greater simplicity?

Apart from its specific doctrines this book is bound to be influential in raising the standard of philosophic workmanship. Many, doubtless, will be offended by the somewhat scant courtesy to all previous philosophy; and the promises of reform in the introduction will be regarded by many others like a set of New Year's resolutions, pious and necessary, but of doubtful efficacy. Few, however, will deny that the authors have done their work in a genuine scientific spirit. The book contains almost no rhetoric. There is no running loose with such catchwords as "experiential," "functional," "dynamic," etc. Problems are minutely and patiently examined for their own sake, and not simply as points in a more or less subtle apology for supposed valuable human interests, like the belief in immortality, freedom, etc. The authors in the main resist the temptation to deal with wholesale affirmations or negations, but insist on a careful examination of the various meanings and situations involved, thus tending to restore *discrimination* as a philosophic virtue. By thus submitting the things of thought to the same careful study as the things of sense receive in the physical sciences, the traditional difference between empiricism and rationalism as methods is

wiped out, and neo-realism may as well be called neo-ration-
alism or neo-empiricism—differing from the older empiricism
in recognizing the immediate reality of the "things of
thought."

Neo-realism is frankly intellectualistic and we may expect
its opponents to call it new-scholasticism, but scholasticism
of a kind has always been needed to police the intellectual
realm and check the riot of anarchic mysticism.

The book before us is not likely to go through twelve
editions within the next year or to receive the Nobel prize
for "idealistic" literature. It lacks the sweep of popular assertions, and is written with conscientious regard for qualification and detail—often most painfully so. It brings no easy
solution to the riddle of the universe, and offers no texts for
pulpit orations. But the discerning will regard it as a notable
contribution to constructive philosophy.

THE NEW REALISM AND
THE PHILOSOPHY OF ROYCE

THE OBJECT of the following brief considerations is not to pass judgment on the value of either of the two philosophies under discussion, but rather to suggest a point of view from which their agreements and differences may appear somewhat more significant than they usually appear to those who approach philosophy from the exclusively epistemologic interest.

If economy of thought be, as Mach and others have it, one of the main objects of science, then philosophic labels like Realism and Idealism are among the most useful instruments of thought. But to those who care for accuracy, these labels appear as snares and stones of stumbling—they are apt to hide from us the important differences which separate many of those who call themselves idealists, and the more important bonds which connect realists and idealists. Vital philosophic achievements, we all know, do not grow out of the effort to spin out the consequences of simple formulae such as those which sum up the distinction between realism and idealism, though such formulae may have a decisive influence in giving direction and form to the effort after coherency and system which is at the heart of philosophy. While philosophy, like law, must of necessity always strive after consistency, it is true as a matter of fact that it never completely attains its goal. The very effort after coherency and system is conditioned for any genuine philosophy by its starting point, the actual complex of intellectual needs growing out of the material of the philosopher's world of experience. If this be so, then the suggestion naturally arises, that the fact that both neo-realism and the philosophy of Royce endeavor to assimilate the general results of modern logical and mathematical studies, may be more significant than the attempt to condense the whole of Royce's philosophy into the dictum that the Absolute is the locus of all our meanings, or neo-realism into the doctrine that objects are independent of our knowledge. The fundamental differences between neo-realism and the philosophy of Royce can from this point of view be traced to their respective attitudes to the problems of religion.

The systematic neglect of mathematics on the part of all great influential philosophies of the nineteenth century is obvious on the most cursory survey. Fichte, Schelling, Hegel, Schopenhauer, Lotze, Mill, Hamilton, Green, Cousin, Comte,[1] Rosmini, all show how social, theologic, and psychologic interests absorbed all attention. Philosophers like Bolzano or Cournot who took the philosophic importance of mathematics seriously, were assigned to obscurity. Now in intellectual affairs, it is difficult to say which is the cause and which the effect. But there can be no doubt that the neglect of mathematics and the prevalence of nominalism and atomism were intimately connected. This can be seen perhaps most clearly in Mill's logic in which the emphasis on particular "facts," "states" of mind, leads to the complete degradation of deduction (and consequently of all exact mathematics) as a source of truth.[2] At any rate, whether we take the phenomenalistic idealism which comes to Mill from Hume, the so-called objective idealism of the Hegelian school of Green and Caird, or the practical idealism of the Neo-Kantians, we find them all assuming that the world which is our starting point is a brute, disconnected manifold; and while these philosophies differ in the method by which the initial atomism is overcome, they all regard the connections or relations of things as a contribution of "the mind" to the world.

Now it would take us far afield to indicate all the difficulties resulting from the assumption that mathematical relations or

[1] I include Comte because though brought up on mathematical physics, his whole philosophy was controlled by practical demands—due to the influence of Saint-Simon.

[2] The exaggerated importance attached to Mill over and above more fruitful logicians like De Morgan and Boole, would not have been possible if philosophers had paid more attention to mathematics.

entities like numbers are mental. But it is clear that this view throws no light at all on the peculiarities of mathematical procedure which distinguish it from physics or psychology. When a mathematician is investigating the property of a given equation or curve, it is precisely as fitting to tell him that he is looking for the product of his own creation as it would have been to have told Leverrier and Adams that in looking for Neptune they were looking for the product of their own mind. Hence, when philosophy could no longer ignore the progress of mathematics and symbolic logic, there was bound to be a reaction against the traditional idealism and a preference for the type of realism that in Greece followed close on the first discovery of mathematical method. Russell's *Principles of Mathematics* and the chapter in his *Problems of Philosophy* dealing with Plato's Doctrine of Ideas, seem to me still the most significant expression of the new yet essentially Platonic realism.[3] To be sure there have been other motives for neo-realism besides the mathematical one, e.g., the natural reaction against the sweeping claims of psychologism, expressed with such admirable self-control by von Meinong. But in emphasizing the objectivity of the relational structure of the real world, neo-realism takes itself completely out of the scope of Professor Royce's dialectical objections against realism, which will be found on close examination to be all arguments against dualistic or atomistic realism that is incompatible with the linkage of facts.

The realistic arguments as to the nature of mathematics were first advanced by Royce in the two volumes of *The World and the Individual,* several years before the appearance of Russell's *Principles of Mathematics.* The mathematician, we are told, is as much a student of given facts as is the

---

[3] For further indications of this I may here refer to my paper on the "Present Situation in the Philosophy of Mathematics," *The Journal of Philosophy,* Vol. VIII (1911), p. 533, constituting Book II, Chapter 1, of *Reason and Nature,* and to my review of *Neo-Realism* in *The Journal of Philosophy,* Vol. X (1913), p. 197, *supra,* p. 109.

chemist or businessman. He is "as faithful a watcher as the astronomer alone with his star" (I, p. 256). The results of his observations abound in the unexpected as much as do the facts of any other field of research. To be sure, Royce adds that what the mathematician watches is *in a sense* the result of his own play or activity; but this "sense" is made clear by the example of the diagram. The mathematician makes his diagram or set of postulates, but he cannot willfully alter the consequences which alone are, after all, the specifically mathematical facts. You may call the spirit from the deep but you cannot control his actions after you have called him.[4] This purely realistic account of mathematics is developed in Professor Royce's address on "The Sciences of the Ideal" (read before the St. Louis Congress), in the monograph on the *Relation of the Principles of Logic to the Foundations of Geometry,* and his essay on "Logic" in the volume entitled the *Encyclopedia of the Philosophical Sciences.* The fruitful character of deductive reasoning as a source of truth appears even in his *Sources of Religious Insight* (pp. 88 ff.).

To those who view Royce's philosophy as a type of Neo-Hegelianism this attention to mathematics may appear as an introjected episode. (Royce's first introduction of mathematical considerations in *The World and the Individual* caused considerable surprise and misgiving doubts among idealists.) But those who have had the good fortune of membership in his logic seminar have learned how characteristic of his thought is the complete objectivity of all logical and mathematical considerations. The truth is that a careful survey of the whole corpus of Professor Royce's writings fully bears out his contention, in the preface to the *Problems of Christianity,* that his philosophy is not in any true sense Hegelian. Such a sur-

[4] In his concept of a common world by means of the process of interpretation, in the second volume of the *Problems of Christianity,* Professor Royce has suggested a method which, if it can successfully be carried out, would overcome the neo-realist antithesis between finding and making propositions true. An adequate discussion of this, however, is not in order before Professor Royce gives us a fuller account of his meaning.

vey seems to me to show how profoundly Royce's philosophy has been influenced, not only by the Kantian doctrine of the primacy of the practical reason,[5] but also by the metaphysic of the *Critique of Pure Reason*. For whatever may be our objections to the Kantian metaphysics, we must not forget that Kant himself began as a mathematical physicist, that he had taught mathematics and that a primary object of his *Critique of Pure Reason* was to show the possibility of mathematics and physics as apodeictic sciences. The Kantian philosophy at least never identified the abstract and the unreal. At any rate it ought to be noted that the very first of Professor Royce's published writings, the *Primer of Logical Analysis,* already shows a strong interest in symbolic logic.

It is, however, precisely Professor Royce's rejection of the Kantian distinction between possible and actual experience that is at the basis of the fundamental divergence between neo-realism and the idealism of Royce. This rejection of the Kantian doctrine seems to me to grow out of the needs of natural theology which looms so large in all of Professor Royce's writings. Religious philosophies are for the most part doctrines of hope or guarantees of the efficacy of moral effort. Hence they tend to assume that the object of our striving is already in some sense actual. This leads to the rejection of all possibility from the nature of the Absolute. The Absolute of Professor Royce's philosophy, however, differs from the realistic God of Aristotle. It is not outside of mundane things but all-inclusive; and this identification of the Good with the Whole leads to the familiar difficulties concerning the problem of evil. It compels us to assume that even now the world is better or richer because of the presence of vice, crime, poverty, disease and all the horrors of war. Such philosophies

[5] This shows itself not only in the conclusion of his paper on Kant in the *Jour. of Spec. Phil.,* but also as the method of postulates in Chs. 9-10 of the *Religious Aspect of Philosophy*. In his general attitude to the importance of the "practical" in philosophy Royce, like James, has been profoundly influenced by Lotze.

have always been sources of strength and comfort to many. Nor can anyone rightly accuse such a philosophy of quietism who notices how few are willing to fight unless they are assured beforehand that victory is in some way certain. Neo-realism, however, does not share this strong faith, so impervious to the vicissitudes of human experience. It is not that neo-realism is hostile to the proper interpretation of religious experience. As I have tried to indicate elsewhere, its logic, with its emphasis on the organizing relations, is a better instrument for social philosophy than any nominalistic philosophy which must contain latent atomism or individualism. But neo-realism sees no evidence that any human community like church or state necessarily embodies our highest goal. The neo-realist lives in a world in which there are all sorts of possibilities of which only a small number succeed in becoming actual, and where all our gods or goods *may* meet with defeat.

SOME DIFFICULTIES IN JOHN DEWEY'S ANTHROPO-CENTRIC NATURALISM

To THOSE who are both conscientious and sensitive, philosophy, like other serious human pursuits, offers difficulties that are often baffling and dispiriting. There are times when not only does the truth which is our objective elude us but when we are tempted to abandon the arduous climb up the uncharted heights and to return instead to the complacent lowlands of Philistia. It is good, therefore, to have our faith strengthened by notable examples of steadfast devotion and heroic attainments. And today no man offers a record of such long, varied and distinguished devotion to philosophy as does John Dewey. For over 57 years he has been publishing the results of his philosophic studies in most diverse fields. With a tireless fidelity and a keen and sensitive eye for the workings of the human mind, his descriptions of what he sees are always penetrating and offer fruit for reflection even in those instances when they do not carry full conviction. It would be a grateful task for me to dwell on his beneficent influence in American life. I know of no one who has done more to keep alive the fundamental ideals of liberal civilization, and I am personally deeply grateful for the illumination and inspiration which I have drawn from his writings and from conversations with him since my boyhood days in 1899. His textbook on Psychology and his early volume on Leibniz were among the first readings that led me to philosophy. And in recent years I have found much nourishing food in his diverse writings on social and political questions, on education and especially on art. The book on Ethics which he wrote with Professor Tufts seems to me to have made that field a living study of actual problems instead of exercises in traditional homiletics, which it used to be in our American colleges. In the field of jurisprudence and in the study of all social institutions he has mightily reinforced the old but ever-needed truth that the Sabbath was made for man, not man for the Sabbath. But my theme is his philosophy of nature, and here, I regret, I cannot follow him.

Some of my difficulties are doubtless due to the limitations of my interests and temperament. To me the central problems of philosophy are the perennial or, if you like, traditional ones of ontology, of the nature of the world into which we are born and which we sooner or later leave. And I am bewildered when I find fundamental cosmic issues ignored or treated only in the interstices of the much more complicated, and to me always illusive, problems of the psychology of human thought or behavior. Many of my differences from Dewey may be differences of emphasis. But in philosophy as in music, emphasis is of the essence. In general I agree with Dewey's rejection of supernaturalism as well as with his humanistic theory of art and morals. But while philosophy to me is no longer theocentric, neither is it as anthropocentric as Dewey's seems to me.

Dewey calls his philosophy humanistic naturalism. In view of the many uses to which the word humanism has recently been applied, to one of which Dewey's whole philosophy is anathema, it seems preferable to call it anthropocentric naturalism. It is undoubtedly a philosophy in which not physical cosmology but social anthropology or a doctrine of human experience plays the central role. It offers no vistas of nature beyond the human scene, and manifests no interest in such questions as the origin and future of our solar system or of life on our earth, or even in the natural conditions which are likely to bring about the disappearance of the human species. Now, it is perfectly legitimate for a philosopher to take a position anywhere and to try to survey the entire realm of being as it appears from that point of view. It is, however, difficult, if not impossible, for any human being to escape the bias which comes from emphasizing the things nearest to him, and not only belittling the things that are foreshortened by their re-

moteness but ignoring or even denying the existence of the
things that are not in his field of interest. More especially is
one tempted to deny, even if only by implication, that other
points of view or perspectives besides one's own can also be
legitimate. That is, I think, more or less the case with humans
generally, and it would have been strange if John Dewey were
an exception. His perspective is essentially that of a moralist,
moving in the humanistic tradition. I have heard him define
philosophy as reflective thought dominated by moral interests.
And in his frequent criticism of other philosophies, he often
emphasizes moral considerations such as the waste of so much
human thought that could be used for the advancement of
human welfare. This leads to a subordination of metaphysical
to moral considerations which seems to me hurtful to both.

My remarks thus naturally fall into two groups. The first
deals with general philosophical difficulties, and the second
with their implications for moral or social theory.

I

AFTER THE GREAT but inadequately informed Hobbes stubbed
his toes by hardy ventures into mathematics and physics,
Locke prudently opened a new way for philosophy by turning it into a psychologic account of our ideas and of the
conduct of our understanding. And Kant only followed when
he made epistemology a necessary precondition for metaphysics, as if a theory of knowledge could possibly be built up
without ontologic assumptions as to the knower and the universe in which knowledge takes place. Except for the important fact that Dewey substitutes a theory of active experience
for the psychology of sensations and their association, he certainly belongs to the Lockian tradition that almost banishes
the cosmologic interest from philosophy. It may at times be
in revolt against the old theology, but it is at one with the
latter in regarding man as the center of the world and viewing

everything else solely in relation to him and to his salvation, in an earthly if not in a heavenly paradise.

In Dewey's actual usage, as in everyone else's, that sacred word of modern philosophy, "experience," is restricted to what happens to human beings or to animals to the extent that they behave like humans. No one speaks of the experience of a dead or lifeless body; and we do not attribute it to the sea, to the rocks, or to the sun before human life appeared on our earth. An experience is therefore a certain kind of event in nature and not the whole of it. And Dewey cannot, as subjective idealists do, identify the existence of an object with our experience of it. He admits the existence of a world before human life came on the scene. But he condemns the contrast between the infinitesimal pettiness of man and the vastness of the stellar universe.[1] Passing over the moral question whether such a contrast is or is not "a cheap intellectual pastime," I should emphatically deny that it is logically illicit. In time as well as in space the existence of man *is* infinitesimal, and the forces at the basis of the stellar universe create and destroy man, while the converse is not true. And if the meaning of objects or events is not purely subjective but is to be found in their objective consequences, the meaning of the stellar universe as distinguished from our apprehension of its meaning is not, except to professional psychologists, exhausted in the emotions or thoughts it arouses in human beings.

Dewey is so intent on proving that everything human is natural that at times he seems to drift into the converse view that all nature or existence can be described in the categories of human experience such as need, uncertainty, precariousness and the like.[2] Possibly the latter attitude is even more strongly influenced by the conviction that the categories of social life are so much richer than those of physical science [3] that they give us a better contact with "reality." But we cannot satisfac-

[1] *Proceedings of the Sixth International Congress of Philosophy*, p. 538.
[2] *Experience and Nature*, pp. 64, 69, 253, 351, and esp. p. 413.
[3] *Philosophy and Civilization*, pp. 77-92.

torily describe the whole cosmos in human terms unless we
believe in thoroughgoing animism, which Dewey does not
profess even in his theory of natural ends. I can, therefore,
see no force at all in his attack on the realists [4] for holding
what seems to me the obvious truth, viz., that search, inquiry,
ignorance and the like are in the field of the personal and the
psychologic but are not traits of *all* existence. While experience is personal not all objects are. Indeed, the categories
in question are not even applicable to all organic beings.
Dewey claims that "It is as much a part of the real being of
atoms that they give rise in time, under increasing complica-
tion of relationships, to qualities of bitter and sweet, pain and
beauty, as that they have at a cross section of time extension,
mass or weight." [5] Now, it should be observed that the assumption that atoms have given rise to the human sense of
beauty is not something that has ever been empirically shown.
It is rather a deduction from the principle of physical determinism which realistic rationalists recognize but which
Dewey cannot completely accept without raising certain difficulties (which I shall mention in the next paragraph). In any
case, if physical objects cause pain or the thrill of beauty in
human beings the reverse is not true. That certain foods are
distasteful, for instance, is a fact that depends on certain chemical factors, while the chemical phenomena do not in the same
way depend on our taste. In general, human pain and the
sense of beauty occur in a passing episode of cosmic history
which might never repeat itself, while extent and mass are
traits that atoms always have. Moreover, I think Dewey
ignores the requisites of precise quantitative thought, which
has done so much to advance physics, when he says "the
domination of man by reverie and desire is as pertinent for
the philosophic theory of nature as is mathematical physics." [6]
No one doubts that human reverie is a natural event, but

---

[4] *Experience and Nature*, p. 69.   [6] *Op. cit.*, first ed., p. 6.
[5] *Op. cit.*, pp. 109-110.

surely it is not one of the great controlling forces of nature that science uses to explain phenomena. For the understanding of the general processes of nature throughout time and space, the existence of human reverie and desire is surely not as illuminating as are considerations of mathematical physics. It illumines the human scene to understand the desire which made men refuse to accept the Copernican astronomy, but it gives us no light on the nature of planetary motion. The solution of human problems depends upon a knowledge of physiology, chemistry, and inorganic physics, but not vice versa.

Can Dewey wholeheartedly accept the principle of physical determinism? In the first place, it is difficult to see how a principle that claims a universal necessity can be fitted into a strictly empirical philosophy, since it cannot be conclusively verified in any single phenomenon or experiment or in any finite number of them. But a more important consideration is that in order to allow human judgments to make a change in the world the latter must be conceived as otherwise incomplete or undetermined. But physical determinism means a closed system of measurable magnitudes, such as ergs, and it is hard to conceive how judgments can be so expressed. Of course, we can abandon the absoluteness of physical determinism and even claim support in Heisenberg's much abused indeterminacy principle. But this not only leaves no basis for confidence in an unbroken chain between atoms and the human sense of beauty, but it weakens the basis for the absolute exclusion of all possible supernatural influence in human development.

Indeed, despite Dewey's insistently sharp dichotomy between his own views and those which he accuses of harboring traces of supernaturalism, he nowhere defines clearly the precise differences between the natural and the supernatural. He seems to think that the invocation of the principle of continuity settles the matter. But what Dewey means by continuity in a pluralistic world containing admitted novelties is obscure to me. At one point he speaks of it as if it were a purely logical principle, so that its denial would involve self-contradiction. But this hardly fits into his own distinction between the logical and the existential. In the essay on the "Influence of Darwin," he argues as if the discovery that some (not all) species have changed in the course of time disproves the Aristotelian logic and the view that the world contains ultimately different kinds of things. But unless we also invoke the opposite principle of discontinuity, continuity would be indistinguishable from what Dewey condemns, namely that all existence is one, and comes under a single concept.

Dewey's predilection for the "thicker" categories of social psychology is closely related to his preference for the method of analyzing experience in the gross as against the traditional way of explaining the actual as a synthesis of simpler elements. The abuse of the latter method is one of the enduring scandals of the intellectual life. But the analytic method is no less subject to limitations. For *what* and *how* we should analyze depend largely on the point of view that we assume to start with. Darwin long ago pointed out that a wrong observation is a much greater hindrance to the progress of science than a wrong theory. And Dewey himself has urged that what are the facts of a given case emerges at the end rather than at the beginning of our investigation. Now there can be no doubt that it is easier to determine the facts in the physical than in the mental or social realm. For not only are the former inherently simpler (since the social includes the physical), but physics also has so many more instruments and methods for eliminating false observations. This makes a consensus (or the elimination of differences of opinion) difficult in the social field. A philosophy therefore which begins with observations on human experience is bound to partake of the uncertainties and controversial differences which abound so much more in what we courteously call social science.

The opposition to all forms of dualism is one of the dominant notes of Dewey's philosophy. In this he relies on the popular philosophy of evolution, though he may also have in mind some of the indications of physiologic psychology. But, while the dualism between conscious and unconscious existence is rejected, he does not postulate any panpsychism to explain the rise of consciousness in an unconscious world. Indeed, in the course of his polemics he sets up dualisms of his own, e.g., that between knowledge and perception, where an evolutionist might expect to find a continuous development of the former from the latter. In war, lines must be sharply drawn. You cannot preach a crusade to free the Zion of experience from the infidel rationalists if you admit that the sacred place is everywhere and that the infidels have some element of the truth in them. Thus, though he must reject the radicalism which attacks the historic past as trivial and harmful, the major part of *Reconstruction in Philosophy* is devoted to drawing a sharp antithesis between what he calls the modern and all previous views of the world, with a rather sweeping rejection of all the latter instead of integrating them in a wider outlook. I shall deal later with his exaggerated contrast between modern and ancient science.

One of the dualisms that Dewey both inherits and develops is that between the existence of particular things and the purely procedural character of logical and mathematical entities or relations.

The term *procedure* or *method* is one of the vaguest in modern philosophy and, next to *reality* and *experience,* most in need of critical challenge for its precise meaning. It is never used in the exact sciences except under precise specifications, so that it was not altogether unjust for Poincaré to remark that physicists discuss their results while their colleagues in the social field discuss their methods. In any case, Dewey himself recognizes that method cannot be completely divorced from subject matter. Yet he adopts the absolute dualism of the formalists that the subject matter of logic or pure mathematics "is not only nonexistential in immediate reference," but is "free from existential reference of even the most indirect de-layed and ulterior kind."[7]

The logical development of mathematics is "the story of [the] liberation of mathematical subject matter from any kind of ontologic reference."[8] But if the marks or sounds, two plus two equals four, had no reference whatsoever to anything be-yond themselves, they would have no meaning. The marks used by mathematicians would not be symbols if they did not symbolize something more than what they themselves are as immediate objects. The objects of mathematics, to be sure, are wider than those of physics, since we can speak intelligibly of nonphysical objects. But if there were no objects of any kind whatsoever, no discourse would be intelligible. There cannot be a possible world or universe of discourse except by reference to some variation from something actual.

If logical and mathematical relations were no part of the nature of things, only something extranatural or a pre-estab-lished harmony could explain their fruitfulness in leading to physical discoveries. On pragmatic grounds there is no reason why Dewey should not reject the detached particular as well as the abstract or detached universal. Do not the relations of an object enter into our experience of it as much as its unique particularity? Universality and particularity are in fact the two poles of existence. Each is necessary but insufficient with-out the other. And at times Dewey explicitly admits that na-ture has its relationships as well as its terms. Indeed, at heart he is at one with Aristotle in holding that the individual apart from universal traits cannot be the object of knowledge.[9] But the undue fear of rationalism often leads him to nominal-ism or conceptualism,[10] as Peirce complained.[11] To say that

[7] *Logic*, p. 396; *Experience and Nature*, pp. 148-149.
[8] *Logic*, p. 397.
[9] *Experience and Nature*, pp. 85, 86.
[10] *Reconstruction*, p. 152.
[11] See "Charles Peirce and a Tentative Bibliography of His Writings," *The Journal of Philosophy*, Vol. XIII (1916), p. 726. It is instructive to note that Peirce's pragmatism allows for purely mental experiments, "con-

the universal is a habit gives us only its psychologic locus, not its denotation. Only our apprehension of the denotation or meaning of an idea is an event which may occur a finite number of times in a personal biography, and as such is the product of human association or interaction. The mathematical and logical relations that we apprehend, e.g., the ratio between the circumference and the radius of a circle, are not human events or habits. They are invariant features of physical nature which we can and do ignore to our peril.

The question how a theorem arises in someone's mind is not the same as the analysis of its meaning or a study of its implications. We cannot by human association or interaction make any proposition the logical consequence of another. We can change the names we give things, but the logical consequences of any set of propositions such as Euclid's axioms do not depend on us. If, from any set of propositions, we could derive any proposition we pleased, nothing could really be said to be proved.

If "meaning is objective as well as universal" [12] it should follow that at least some universals are objective. The fact that they are illuminating or instrumental does not prove that they are not also constitutive.

The traditions of empiricism, the distrust of universals or abstractions, often leads Dewey to an inadequate appreciation of the role of mathematics. The following passage is an instance.

"When men insisted upon judging astronomical phenomena by bringing them directly under established truths, those of geometry, they had no astronomy, but only a private esthetic construction. Astronomy began when men trusted themselves to embarking upon the uncertain sea of events and were willing to be instructed by changes in the concrete." [13]

ceivable consequences," which Dewey cannot allow if he follows his opposition to the usual distinction between the mental and the physical.

[12] *Experience and Nature,* p. 188.

[13] *Human Nature,* pp. 242-243.

But history shows that men sailed or guided their camels by the light of the stars before a science of astronomy was born. It was precisely when the phenomena were subsumed under the laws of geometry that the science began.

As a psychologist interested primarily in the way men think and acquire knowledge, Dewey views logic from the point of view of human inquiry. This is an important field of study, and it is not necessary for me to add to the many deserved encomia as to the value of Dewey's contribution to it. But there are two difficulties which I find in his view. The first has to do with the ignoring or denial of the ontologic basis of logical procedure, and the second difficulty is with his denial that scientific inquiry can be defined in terms of knowledge.

Like the positivists Dewey rejects as ridiculous the view that logic prescribes how we should think [14] (which, it seems to me, is precisely what logic does indicate, if we wish to avoid certain fallacies). Instead, he offers us the view that logic is a description of those methods of inquiry that are successful. But what is a method of inquiry? Science knows of methods of verification but there are no methods of discovery. If there were such, all we need would be discovered, and we would not have to wait for rare men of genius. Now the vagueness of the term *method* as a description of actual human thinking is not at all clarified by the introduction of the word *successful*. What is the test as to when an inquiry is successful? Surely not anything practical in the ordinary sense of the word; for in practical affairs we often get sufficiently satisfactory (though not accurate) information by all sorts of accidents of good fortune in no way connected with the rules of logic. Even in scientific work men frequently arrive at the truth by logically false reasoning, as Galileo did in his argument that the velocity acquired by a falling body does not vary directly with the space through which it falls.

Shall we say that in the long run those methods which give

---

[14] *Reconstruction*, p. 136.

us most truth are bound to be selected by a sort of survival of the fittest? That would give us no logical test before the run was sufficiently long, and how long that is no one knows. But, in any case, such a view would be an historical generalization for which I should like to see more evidence. There is certainly a good deal of evidence to the contrary in the decline of Greek science. Assuredly, prejudice, superstition, and logical fallacies persist; and Dewey himself has in one instance at least found a pejorative psychogenesis or bad ancestry for a certain view of philosophy to be a more effective argument against it than a logical refutation.[15] It is well for us if in practice we follow the rules of logic, but their validity does not depend upon how men actually behave.

Dewey himself rejects certain doctrines as self-contradictory. This rejection is surely not based on the assumption that it is impossible to think or express contradictions, for that is precisely what the holders of these doctrines are accused of actually doing. The real objection is that there cannot possibly exist anything objective denoted by these self-contradictory doctrines. The principle of contradiction therefore asserts something in regard to existence and not merely in regard to thought or that logical monstrosity, language that has no reference to anything other than itself that it can denote or mean. Logic may thus be viewed as the simplest chapter in ontology, as a study of the exhaustive possibilities of all being. Its laws are not derived from our intentions but express the fact that as regards determinate being or existence certain combinations are possible and others impossible. A world in which everything was possible, and nothing impossible, would be a chaos; and science and common practice cannot proceed without assuming a world in which definite or determinate relations are discoverable. From the laws of logic we cannot deduce any specific matters of fact; but, without assuming that the laws of logic are relevant to existence, no inquiry can

15 *Op. cit.*, p. 24.

be launched, much less concluded. Logic indicates necessary but not sufficient determinants of empirical existence.

My second difficulty is with Dewey's assertion that knowledge is to be defined in terms of inquiry and not vice versa. Here as in other instances, Dewey's affirmation seems to me perfectly legitimate, but I see no justification for the denial; nor does Dewey carry it out consistently. Significant or scientific inquiry cannot take place except on the assumption of knowledge already had, together with knowledge of what kind of an answer would be relevant to our question. We must know what to look for if we are to discover anything. And previous knowledge of nature is necessary to understand what we observe. My difficulties increase when, to these observations which are duly recognized by Dewey himself on many occasions, I add his exclusively prospective view of knowledge, that "consequences, not antecedents, supply meaning and verity."

That the logical consequences of a proposition are essential to its meaning seems to me an important insight which we owe to many thinkers from Socrates to Peirce. But that the antecedents of a proposition do not "supply meaning and verity" seems surprising when coming from one who places so much emphasis on the psychogenesis or origin of our ideas. In any case, judgments of probability, the abstemious empiricist's staple food, are meaningless apart from the antecedent evidence which forms their premises. Dewey maintains that previous knowledge is held subject to use and is at the service of the discovery which it makes possible, and has to be adjusted to the latter but not the latter to it. Here, as in so many other passages of Dewey's writings, he seems to me to add hasty negations to sound affirmations. Most emphatically is it true that a past generalization must be adjusted to new factual discoveries. But it is equally true that new scientific discoveries do and must involve adjustments to previous knowledge. And the empiricists at least should admit the historic fact that scientific discoveries are generally not made by ignorant people who decide to follow the Baconian method of getting rid of all anticipations of nature and starting with a free or empty mind, but only by those who do have knowledge and who have been able to give intense thought to the subject in hand. Scientific discoveries are interpretations of observations, and these interpretations involve assumptions as to the nature of our instruments and as to the constant relations of the observed to other phenomena of nature. When Lavoisier burned certain substances and found that their weight increased, that did not by itself overthrow the theory of phlogiston. That result came only because other antecedent truths of chemistry made the explanation in terms of the oxygen theory a simpler one. When a new discovery upsets an old principle it is only because the old principle is thus proved to be inconsistent with other *known* truths. The bending of light rays overthrows Newton's formula for the law of gravitation, but only when the bending of light rays is viewed as a consequence of hitherto accepted principles of optics. Without accepting these old truths Newton's gravitational formula could not be impugned by new facts.

Dewey's philosophy may be viewed as one of the many efforts since Hume to introduce the experimental method of the physical sciences into philosophy and moral subjects. These attempts generally proceed on the naïve assumption that the only reason this has not been done before is that people didn't think of it or were prevented by sheer prejudice or by Aristotle. It is doubtless true that where human values are felt intensely most of us are unwilling to pursue the detached objectivity of science. But the human field is also inherently more complex and intractable. It is difficult, if not impossible, to vary its factors one at a time as we can in the inorganic field. Even the biologic question of heredity becomes more difficult of solution when we consider the human species. The outstanding fact is that we cannot experiment on human beings as freely as we can on hydrogen gas or guinea pigs. I once heard T. H. Morgan take Raymond Pearl to task for leaving his fruit flies to take up such a poor biologic specimen as man. Moreover, even when social experiments are tried, the pragmatic test of truth, or the appeal to experience, is indecisive as to fundamentals. For the question whether a doctrine works satisfactorily or not is itself determined by faith in it. Thus the doctrines of Christianity and Islam are at many points in direct opposition; and many peoples in Asia, Africa, and Eastern Europe have changed from the former to the latter. But in the main, each party finds that the experience of thirteen centuries proves it right. The case is similar in regard to Catholicism and Protestantism. And in our own day believers in democracy, fascism, and communism are equally convinced that the actual course of experience is proving their view to be the only true one. And this state of affairs may continue indefinitely as it has in the field of religion.

The hope of those who, following Bacon, aim at a reconstruction of philosophy on the model of experimental science, is generally supported by a conventional but apocryphal history which is plausible only because ancient and medieval science are for linguistic reasons not popularly accessible. On one occasion Dewey maintained that ancient science was demonstrative, while the lifeblood of modern science is discovery. Now I submit that this is neither historically true nor can it ever be so. Mathematics, the most demonstrative of the sciences, grows by successive discoveries, and has proved the most fruitful source of even physical discoveries. For mathematical and logical relations are as objective matters to be investigated as are the velocities of the stars. Nor is it true, as is asserted by popular historians and by scientists when away from their laboratories on a philosophic picnic, that the Greeks did not resort to experiment. The work of Hippocrates, Archimedes, Hero, Hipparchus, and Eratosthenes amply indicates the contrary. Even Pythagoras had to experiment to discover the laws of musical harmony. It required experiment to determine the effects of diet, exercise, and climate on health and disease. It required refined measurement (which is still essential for exact experiment) to decide the choice between rival theories of astronomy such as those of epicycles and excentric motion, to determine the precession of the equinoxes, or the actual length of a degree of latitude on our earth. Moreover, an actual reading of the work of Copernicus, Kepler, Galileo, and Newton fails to justify the popular legend that the science of the sixteenth and seventeenth centuries was revolutionary in its attitude to previous science. It is a myth to suppose that modern science arose when it suddenly occurred to a few men to discard the authority of Aristotle and to examine nature for themselves. That was the bright idea of the lawyer, courtier, and literary artist, Francis Bacon, and it got him nowhere in actual science. Indeed, it made him ignore and even oppose the most significant scientific achievements of his day, such as the Copernican astronomy, the mechanical interpretation of physics, the physiologic discoveries of his own personal physician, Harvey, and the pioneer researches of Gilbert, whose writings were entrusted to him. If we read Copernicus' own work we see that he only revived the Pythagorean astronomy, that he accepted the method of Ptolemy, which is after all still the method of mathematical physics, and that his so-called revolution was after all only a simplification of Ptolemy by reducing the number of epicycles. Kepler was not only profoundly influenced by neo-Platonism, but one of his principal works is a commentary on the optics of a medieval theologian, Vitello. To Galileo and Newton, Euclid and the other Greek mathematicians were the very basis of all physical science. It is amazing how relatively few mechanical experiments all these men made and how much they were influenced by the idea that the book of nature was written in mathematical terms so that the object of science was to find out this simple underlying mathematical pattern. Anyone who has ever tried to repeat Galileo's experiment of rolling balls on an inclined plane will need no assurance that without the prior faith in the simplicity of natural laws Galileo's actual results would have proved nothing at all. For under the conditions of his experiment the necessary degree of accuracy cannot possibly be attained. Even more is this the case with the supposed dropping of two weights from the Tower of Pisa. To prove what it is generally supposed to have proved, it would have been necessary to create a perfect vacuum by eliminating all the air between the tower and the earth. In any medium such as air or water, the resistance to and retardation of a falling body does depend on its mass, as Lucretius clearly pointed out in antiquity and as anyone can observe for himself if not prevented by reliance on the popular anti-Aristotelian mythology. Note that I am not denying the importance of experiment in modern or in ancient science, nor that, in America especially, many more men are now engaged in laboratories. But I think that a due regard for the essential role which mathematical or theoretical development plays in experimental work is not only necessary to explain the growth of science, modern or ancient, but also to remove the false dualism between experiment and rational determination.

Modern science has not abandoned the basic Hellenic idea of a constant order, law, or relation, in the flux of phenomena, nor has it adopted the cult of the limitless infinite, nor the even more recent illusion of function without substance, the grin without the cat. And it is simply not true that "Change rather than fixity is now a measure of 'reality' or energy of being." [16] According to the principle of relativity there is just as much rest and permanence in the world as there is motion and change, since neither set of categories has any physical meaning apart from the other. And even in the older physics, potential energy, the energy of position, is as real as kinetic energy. The subordination of one to the other is as foreign to physical science as the subordination of the north to the south pole.

When I read the *Politics* or the biologic treatises of Aris-

[16] *Op. cit.*, p. 61.

totle, or even works of medieval scholastics such as Adelard of Bath, Albertus Magnus, or Maimonides, I fail to find anything radically novel in the appeal to experience. And in view of Dewey's rejection of any dualism between reason and experience,[17] I cannot understand his own sharp contrast between empiricism and rationalism. The former, he says, consists in showing or pointing or coming upon the thing discussed, while the latter assumes the primacy and ultimacy of logical thought and findings. I see no basis for assuming these two attitudes to be incompatible, since Dewey himself admits that deduction or the logic that governs it is one of the things pointed out, found and shown.[18] In fact, the logical impossibility of deducing material propositions from purely formal ones was first brought out most clearly and cogently, not by the philosophers of the empirical school, but by the movement for logical rigor in mathematics. And the distrust of self-evident premises goes back to the great rationalist Leibniz. Even Kant, for whom Dewey seldom has a really kind word, has insisted that concepts without percepts are empty, just as percepts without concepts are blind. And to the extent that Dewey, though rejecting the old faculty-psychology, accepts the interdependence or polar character of the perceptual and the conceptual, that in every specific inquiry experimental and *a priori* considerations are both inextricably involved, I agree with him as he does with Kant. But I think that the absolute dualism between the empirical and the rational with its rather unmeasured apotheosis of the former, should yield to a more precise analysis of the distinction between history on the one hand, and logic or pure mathematics on the other.

In challenging Dewey's account of the history of science as a support for his philosophy,[19] I by no means admit the legitimacy of the extent to which he often treats the birth certificate of a doctrine as a guide to its truth. The fact

[17] *Op. cit.,* p. 100.
[18] *Experience and Nature,* first ed., p. 10.
[19] *The Quest for Certainty,* pp. 92 ff.; *Reconstruction,* Ch. III.

that geometry arose out of surveying does not determine the truth or falsity of any theorem in it. But I do not want to discuss here the general validity of the passage from the chronologic to the logical order which an uncritical acceptance of Hegel and romantic evolutionism has made so popular. One specific point, however, is noteworthy. Dewey argues against the belief in a single ultimate and final good, that it is an intellectual product of the feudal organization, which is disappearing.[20] Now, I should not admit that any doctrine, say, for instance, that of representative government, is bad because it originated in a system of society which no longer exists. The present worth of any doctrine should be examined on its own merits in the light of present conditions. But the assertion, that the doctrine of a single ultimate and final good does depend upon feudalism, is certainly not true. It is found among ancient and modern thinkers who have not lived under feudalism.

Brought up in the Protestant tradition, Dewey regards the Catholic philosophy of St. Thomas as overthrown. "It is already dim, faded, and remote." But to millions of men, as intellectual as ourselves, it is still the only true philosophy. I do not myself accept the Catholic philosophy and my people have no pleasant memories of the Inquisition. But philosophic issues have to be met in the intellectual arena, and I think St. Thomas and Duns Scotus worthy of more attention than some of our minor contemporaries. Neglect is not a philosophic refutation.

Here a word may be added on the close connection which Dewey sees between experience and democracy. One may share his ardent and lyric devotion to democracy in politics and social life without admitting its relevance to science and philosophy. After all, Archimedes, Copernicus, Galileo, Kepler, Harvey, Newton, Lavoisier, Gauss and a host of others did not live in democracies. Nor can I admit the validity of the

20 *Reconstruction,* p. 162.

current appeal to the common man as the ultimate judge of issues which he has never examined with sufficient care. Indeed, if the views of the common man were satisfactory, why should philosophy as critical reflection have arisen on Dewey's own theory? When the common man has good sense, or the wisdom of humility, he recognizes his limitations and is willing to learn from those who have devoted more time and attention to philosophy than he has.

Dewey's preoccupation with the human or moral function of science, and his polemic against the spectator or contemplative theory of knowledge, lead to three characteristic instrumentalist doctrines, namely, that knowledge and reflection arise only to enable us to get out of trouble,[21] that science grows out of practical daily needs, and that philosophy is a reflex of the civilization of its period and should be directed to illumine contemporary social problems. These doctrines seem to me partial or half-truths that are misleading in their one-sidedness and in need of serious correction not only for the sake of more accurate truth but also for the sake of that humane liberalism which is at the heart of Dewey's whole intellectual effort.

As to the first point, philosophers and scholars are, doubtless, apt to magnify the role that knowledge plays in ordinary experience. But that is no reason for asserting that it is never its own purpose or justification. The desire to know for its own sake, to satisfy idle curiosity, is a fact of human nature. Children show it and adults, too, when not educated or shamed out of it. Common men and good women are interested in ascertaining baseball or football scores or in what was said or done by certain prominent statesmen, by movie stars, or even by our less prominent neighbors. We do not always read our daily newspapers, biographies, histories, or works on philosophy for the sake of any application. And sustained reflection or study may occur more often in our

[21] *Essays*, pp. 20, 73; *Reconstruction*, pp. 23, 30, 53; *Experience and Nature*, pp. 51, 76.

leisure than when we are in practical trouble. Indeed, the latter is apt to prove an obstacle to persistent intellectual inquiry.

Invention or progress in science depends on a certain amount of leisure, and freedom from economic or vital pressure. Disinterested curiosity is certainly one of the dominant, if not the dominant, among the forces which lead men to science and make progress in it possible. The history of many branches of science, such as electricity and magnetism from the days of Thales to those of Gilbert and of Faraday or paleontology from Xenophanes to our own day, shows how remote they were in origin from technologic interests. I am not denying that many problems of mathematics and theoretic physics have in fact been suggested by practical needs and have found useful applications. I am denying the universal proposition that all have been. Moreover, men do not make discoveries even in medical sciences such as pathology solely because they are anxious to relieve human suffering. We cannot solve problems of the pathology or chemistry of disease except by concentrating our attention entirely on the determining factors of the process. To be thinking of the human values of the results would be an irrelevance and therefore a hindrance to the investigation itself. Nor is it even true that men always do or should choose those problems which they think will contribute most to human welfare. Men get interested in certain mathematical, physical, chemical, or biologic problems, in the same way that those with less time and less intellectual equipment get interested in solving conundrums, crossword puzzles, charades, or detective mysteries, the great difference being that the subject matter and procedure of science is so much richer and more sustaining in its interest. To be sure, science today has become a professional occupation; but that does not deny that the great contributors to science, men like Newton, Lavoisier, Cavendish, or Willard Gibbs, have been drawn to it by an inner urge like that which leads men to compose music. And one of the greatest of recent contributors to medical science, Theobold Smith, once declared that, despite his very favorable official position, all the research he ever did was done by stealth. Devotion to science is often an infatuation or love which does not reckon with external consequences.

It cannot be too strongly emphasized that relatively few branches of science have had practical applications; and of many realms, such as the theory of prime numbers or the proof of theorems such as Fermat's, it is hard to imagine how they can possibly ever have any. It is told of a great mathematician that, when he announced the solution of a famous mathematical problem, someone asked him of what use it was, whereat he replied: "Thank God, it has none." A great American physicist is said to have dropped the study of radioactivity when he found it had practical application in medicine. Whether these specific instances are historical or not, I cannot vouch. But they are typical of many men engaged in pure science, who, with the most benevolent attitude to the social needs of their day, still feel ill at ease in the field of applied science where the immediate, the practical, and the approximate rather than the ideal of rigorous accuracy is dominant. In the minds of some men like Einstein the pursuit of science is motivated by what has been called cosmic emotion, which is akin to certain religious feelings that are highly individual and not at all social.

In the light of the foregoing considerations no account of the history of philosophy seems even plausible which neglects the role that curiosity about cosmic issues (or Aristotelian wonder) has played in its origin and maintenance. And Dewey seems to me to be straining the facts when he contends "that philosophy originated not out of intellectual but out of social and emotional material." [22] The origin of Greek philosophy is certainly connected with the interest in abstract mathematics and cosmology as distinguished from any technical or

[22] *Reconstruction,* p. 25.

social applications. Thales and other Ionian thinkers doubtless had political and economic interests. But there is no evidence that these controlled the direction of their philosophy,
or that their thought was dominated by the apologetic attempt to justify existing institutions by harmonizing them
with practical knowledge, as Dewey's account in the first
chapter of his *Reconstruction in Philosophy* would have it.
Melissos was a successful admiral; but his philosophy came
from Parmenides and Zeno, who seem in their metaphysical
speculations to have turned their backs on human affairs.
Moreover, the exaltation of pure theory is explicitly professed by Aristotle as well as by Plato. It is only in the days
of its decline, in later Greek and Roman times, that philosophy became almost entirely concerned with guiding human
conduct.

I think it rather important in this connection to challenge
the view, fashionable since Hegel, that the philosophy of any
period is the reflex of the civilization under which the individual philosophers live. Reflections on the nature of number, time, space, mind, matter, and knowledge do not vary
with political and economic views or changes. The outstanding fact is rather that in every age in which there is any
philosophy at all relatively few are interested in it, and among
them the most divergent views prevail, just as between idealists, realists, and instrumentalists in our own day, not to mention skeptics, mystics, authoritarians, and many others. The
common institutions under which the men of a given period
live cannot be the sufficient cause for what they do *not* have
in common. On the other hand, the elements common to
great thinkers of different countries and periods seem far
more important for philosophy than those any one of them
may share with his contemporaries who opposed or ignored
him. Great philosophers speak to all time; only the minor ones
are dated. Few generations have been interested in Plato's
criticisms of the electoral machinery of the Greek democracies;
but his doctrine of Ideas has, for good or ill, stirred men's

[161]

minds throughout the ages. Kant has more in common with Plato than with Frederick the Great; Hobbes has more in common with Democritus than with Digby; and Bradley is more intimately related to Parmenides or Spinoza than to Herbert Spencer or William James. That which unites ancient and modern skeptics, materialists or idealists, or Hindu, Greek, Hebrew, Arabic, and Christian mystics, is more significant for philosophic truth than the external resemblances which a number of them may have because they lived at the same time. Not only do many philosophers frequently read their ancients more than their contemporaries, but there are certain differences of temper, say, between the tough-minded and the tender-minded, which prevail in all ages. Thus many a man has turned to philosophy precisely because he was not like his neighbors or even his brothers absorbed in the passing problems of the day. And Dewey admits this when he condemns them for it, a condemnation which many of them would certainly accept as a tribute to their real wisdom.

It is interesting to note that in a concrete case, namely, as to the difference between Russell's philosophy and his own, he vehemently rejects the explanation in terms of English aristocracy and American democracy and appeals rather to the fact of different intellectual interests, Russell's in mathematics, and his own in the experimental method of obtaining knowledge. Even Hegel's view of the state may be far more influenced by the reading of Aristotle and Luther than by the actual Prussian state with which he came in contact rather late in life.

In this connection I must confess my inability to follow the strange doctrine that "philosophy is occupied with meaning rather than with truth." I find it difficult to reconcile this contention which makes the truth of the great philosophic systems relatively unimportant,[23] with his own persistent effort to refute them. Surely, his objection to them is not that

___

[23] *Proceedings of the Sixth International Congress of Philosophy*, pp. 537, 540.

what they have said is meaningless, since as philosophies they are admittedly significant; and in any case the meaningless cannot be refuted. His actual arguments are intended to prove that previous philosophies assert things which are not true, for example, that perception is a form of knowledge. If the method of sound philosophy is that of science, the distinction between the true and the false is the essential question. The difficulty is not removed by making truth play a negative role in philosophy. Of course, any philosophy that does not suffer from what Santayana calls nearsighted sincerity must extend its vision beyond the actually verified results of the special sciences. But hypotheses or even imaginative anticipations of the progress of science are true or false. I cannot see how meanings without any claim to possible truth can be the content of even the most speculative, much less empirical philosophy. When we speak of the meaning of the Hellenic civilization we point to the wider historic antecedents and consequences of Greek institutions. But such historic connections did or did not take place, and assertions about them as well as about the history of philosophy are therefore true or false. And so are those assertions about the wider world which is the subject of philosophy.

II

WE COME NOW to the question about the moral value of theoretic science and speculative philosophy pursued for their own sake without regard to their application in human affairs. Orthodox pietists, puritan moralists, and efficiency-minded philosophers are agreed in condemning these pursuits as a waste; and to call philosophy an indoor sport commonly passes as a condemnation of it. This is entirely opposed to Dewey's humane ethics. He has impressively, and to my mind convincingly, emphasized the importance of sport, play, and art as indispensable for moral sanity.[24] He has repeatedly and quite rightly insisted that by practical he does not mean narrow ends of the bread-and-butter type. And more recently he has disclaimed the intention to subordinate knowledge to action. But I think it is fair to distinguish between an author's conscious intention (of which he is the sole judge) and the bearing of what he has actually said, which is an objective social affair. For words, like arrows, have effects not always identical with the intention of the one who sets them loose. And I do not see how anyone can read Dewey's works without finding explicit as well as implicit subordination of theoretic knowledge to practical moral ends. The following passages seem quite typical. "For in an experience where values are demonstrably precarious, an intelligence that is not a principle of emphasis and valuation (an intelligence which defines, describes, and classifies merely for the sake of knowledge), is a principle of stupidity and catastrophe." [25] An interest in the theory of knowledge for its own sake is characterized as "a luxury and hence a social nuisance and disturber." [26] He rejects the view of the new realism that thinking "is instrumental simply to the knowledge of objects" and insists that it is "instrumental to a control of the environment." [27] Natural science "is something to be pursued not in a technical and specialized way for what is called truth for its own sake, but with the sense of its social bearing, its intellectual indispensableness. It is technical only in the sense that it provides the technique of social and moral engineering." [28] Indeed, his whole *Reconstruction in Philosophy* and the essay on the *Recovery of Philosophy* are devoted to the thesis that philosophy should be "a method of understanding and rectifying specific social ills." [29] He pours his scorn on contemplative surveys of existence, on monkish detachment, on the otiose observer who is content to be concerned with things past and

---

[24] *Human Nature and Conduct,* p. 161.   [27] *Essays in Exp. Logic,* p. 30.
[25] *Influence of Darwin,* p. 44.   [28] *Reconstruction,* p. 173.
[26] *Op. cit.,* pp. 298-299.   [29] *Op. cit.,* p. 124.

done with. "Philosophy is of account only if, like everyday knowing, and like science it affords guidance to action." [30] To study history or to dwell upon the past for its own sake is condemned as a "substitution of the reminiscence of old age for effective intelligence." [31] The spectator view of knowledge is condemned as irresponsible estheticism, "a purely compensatory doctrine," a consolation for those "held back through lack of courage from making their knowledge a factor in the determination of the course of events." [32] If we were to adopt a clever argument of Russell, we might be tempted to say of Dewey that, having by definition ruled out the possibility of contemplative knowledge, its occurrence must be characterized as wicked. But that would not only be unfair but would miss what seems to me the underlying motive, and that is a strong sense of the social responsibility of the philosopher as a condition for making philosophy itself more alive and substantial. I should not wish to deny that social problems can be viewed as offering genuine philosophic issues; I have made some attempts in that direction myself. But I cannot agree that this is the only proper field for philosophic reflection. Taken literally Dewey's attitude on this point, or perhaps more accurately his expressions, would in principle condemn not only pure mathematics and all theoretic science that has not found and may never find any practical application, but also all music and fine art that has not been devoted to influencing the course of social events.

Such impoverishment of human life is obviously far from the intention of one so devoted to the tradition of liberalism. But opposition to the spectator-theory of knowledge, and zeal for social betterment, together with what may without offense be called an anti-Aristotelian complex, lead Dewey to decidedly illiberal expressions like the foregoing. I do not suppose that he would condemn climbing mountains for the sake of the vistas which we can obtain from their peaks. Why

---

[30] *Creative Intelligence*, p. 60.   [32] *Reconstruction*, p. 117.
[31] *Creative Intelligence*, p. 14.

then should he condemn its intellectual analogue or extension, Aristotelian contemplation or theoretic vision, which is the exercise of an intense human energy and adds by its very aloofness a much-needed serene sweetness and noble joy to human life? That the philosopher, scientist, or artist should subordinate all his thought to the welfare of the community in which he lives is, alas, the demand not only of the increasing number of partisans of the totalitarian state but of popular opinion in our and other democratic countries. In popular education for instance it would subordinate the claims of historic truth to those of patriotism. Hence those interested in the values of the intellectual life must resist the multitude which is ever ready to sacrifice philosophy, pure science and other forms of nonutilitarian learning for all sorts of immediate ends of a petty practical kind. At all times and places combatants in the social conflicts of the day despise the neutral. And the philosopher must often remain neutral in thought if he has a conscientious regard for intellectual integrity and recognizes that neither side has proved its case and that he himself has not sufficient information to decide all the questions at issue. What the various parties in our social conflicts generally demand of the philosopher is not enlightenment (which might possibly dampen the fierce ardor of the struggle) but partisan support; and when the philosopher does that he renders little aid to his party and grievous harm to his philosophy. This does not mean that we may not join any church or political party or other active group with a social program. Being a philosopher no more than being a mathematician, musician, or clergyman excuses one from ordinary domestic, civic, and political obligations. But the special duty of the philosopher is to put the pursuit of truth first whether his fellow citizens are interested or not; and this often requires ethical neutrality or indifference to the issues of the day. It may be well to be sensitive to the needs and problems of those with whom one is associated. But that does not mean that we must yield to the nonphilosophic as to what problems are most important.

We too are men, and we ought to know that the market place does not exhaust the whole meaning of life.

As against Dewey's emphasis on the philosopher's participation in the problems of (other) men, I think it necessary to adopt a more critical attitude to the notion of the social responsibility of philosophy, and to the optimistic view of the power of human intelligence, in the face of nature's obstacles. Especially must we realize the limitations of atomic empiricism in social philosophy.

No sensitive spirit can fail to be stirred by Dewey's eloquent plea that we help our fellow men in the bitter struggle for a better world. But what should philosophy do about it? Must one who cannot swim jump into the whirlpool to save a drowning man? Surely it is not one's duty as a philosopher to plunge into the maelstrom of social efforts without adequate knowledge as to what would be a better world and what will actually bring it about. To accept blindly from our fellow men their current attitudes as to what is good or better is certainly not the way to bring them salvation. And surely, an empirical philosopher has no reason to feel that he can easily obtain adequate knowledge to solve all the problems of politics, economics, social hygiene, and other difficulties which have troubled mankind for thousands of years. Dewey is aware of this but boldly asserts: "Better it is for philosophy to err in active participation in the living struggles and issues of its own age and time than to maintain an immune, monastic impeccability." [33] I cannot share this preference. It seems to me foolish for philosophy deliberately to choose to fall into error when it can save itself by suspending judgment, by recognizing that the practical necessity for making a choice does not remove our ignorance. Nor does wisdom require us to be frightened by epithets such as "monastic," "ivory tower," "escapist," or "compensatory." It is wisdom to leave a room that is filled with suffocating smoke,

[33] *Essays in Honor of William James,* p. 77.

and in dark ages monasticism kept alive the remnants of civilization. And I should think monastic impeccability far more justifiable both for philosophy and social sanity, than adding to the already large fund of error about issues that our fellow men think important.

Philosophy according to Dewey "must deny and eject that intelligence which is naught but a distant eye, registering in a remote and alien medium the spectacle of nature and life." [34] I venture to assert that relatively few sensitive and reflective minds have gone through this world without often feeling alien in its fetid air and needing to escape for a while into a rare and higher atmosphere. "My kingdom is not of this world" is an important element in a truly human life, a redemption from deadly worldliness. And most people do require quasi-monastic conditions in their study in order to engage in concentrated intellectual work which is not possible in the hubbub of crowds. The wisdom of humility requires that the philosopher should not unduly exalt the importance of his special vocation. But neither should he envy the man of action, the one whose maxim is: "For God's sake, stop theorizing and do something practical!" Nor am I impressed with the argument that philosophers are economic parasites unless they direct their reflection towards practical objectives. We have as much a right to philosophize as to pray, to hear music, or to be spectators at dramatic performances. No one is really paid for philosophizing. Some, though not all, philosophers have been employed as teachers; but I should be surprised to learn that any got excessively rich thereby. The upkeep of philosophers is far from being such a staggering burden on society as to demand serious attention.

Though Dewey would hardly subscribe to Emerson's idealistic Platonism and the doctrine that the oversoul is everything, he shares Emerson's benign attitude in regard to the unconquerable natural ills which have dogged human ex-

[34] *Creative Intelligence*, p. 66.

istence throughout the ages. He rejects the view that our appetites and desires are the manifestations of unruly nature. For that would make democracy impossible.[35] "Man is capable, if he will but exercise the required courage, intelligence, and effort, of shaping his own fate. Physical conditions offer no insurmountable barriers." [36] But, if that were the case, why has not mankind exercised its intelligence to remove the stupid cruelties which darken the lives of men and women in our day as much as ever, in countries that are at peace as well as those at war? If the cause is not in nature, human or nonhuman, what is there left but to invoke a supernatural source of evil? We are told to have faith in the active tendencies of the day.[37] But these tendencies may destroy all the values of civilization. As a temporalist Dewey puts the Golden Age in the future rather than in the past. Such hope strengthens men, and it cannot be refuted. But the philosopher who piously visits the cemetery of human hopes may well shake his head. And this attitude is not dismissed by calling it a counsel of despair. There is strength as well as solace in fearlessly looking at things as they are. But in the end no philosophy is really humane, or avoids needless cruelty, unless it recognizes the inevitability of human suffering, defeat, death, and destruction and provides some anodyne through wisely cultivated resignation.

So long as human beings lack omniscience they will lack omnipotence and will therefore have to face insuperable difficulties and evils. The acceptance of the inevitable, ceasing "to kick against the pricks," seems to me the great wisdom of the old religious teachers who, despite their supernaturalisms, had keen appreciations of the problems of actual living. This does not deny that all human beings do and should pursue what may, in the broader sense, be called economic ends, i.e., the increase of the means for the desirable kind of life. But human beings also have a craving not only for worship,

[35] *Influence of Darwin,* p. 59.
[36] *Reconstruction,* p. 49.
[37] *Op. cit.,* p. 212.

but for subordinating themselves so as to avoid the intolerable distraction which often arises when we have to decide on the basis of imperfect knowledge. Indeed the history of such movements as Islam or Calvinism shows how submission can liberate human energies. No man is as happy and energetic as the one who is a glad slave to his beloved, whether it be a person or a great impersonal cause. For this reason it would be hazardous to deny that human beings have probably derived as much happiness from accepting their lot as from efforts, so often tragically vain, to improve it.

I am familiar with the argument that if we abandoned all forms of resignation and strenuously devoted ourselves instead to the improvement of actual conditions there would be no need for resignation. But this seems to me wishful thinking requiring much more evidence than has ever been offered for it. Doubtless there is such a thing as unwise submission. But who will deny that there is also an unwise obstinacy in refusing to accept our limitations and thus wasting life in efforts that are fruitless if not worse? We in America are especially in need of realizing that perpetual motion is not the blessed life and that the hustlers may not be the only ones, nor perhaps even the first, to enter the kingdom of heaven. I am not arguing against the necessity of effort and work. But I do want to suggest a doubt about any moral system that is too social and does not recognize the just claims of rest, of vacations from the strenuous life, of retreats or escapes if you like, from the depressing horrors of the human scene and its brutal struggles. Like other intellectual workers the philosopher must break away from the crowd, even as Jesus, filled with compassion for the multitude, retires alone to the mountain to pray. Why should philosophy deny us any private nook in this wide universe which the soul may for a while call its own?

Dewey's optimism is based on a "positive respect for human nature when the latter is associated with scientific knowledge." [38] He greatly admires Bacon, who is frequently praised for his efforts to free philosophy from idle speculation and logic chopping and to bring it down to man's business and bosoms, so that knowledge of nature may become a power for human welfare. But Bacon's Utopia of many men working to advance man's control of nature has been largely realized in the many researches which apply modern science to machinery. And the result has certainly not been free from new horrors (in peace as well as in war) added to human life thereby. Dewey, of course, is aware of some of the failures of the Baconian Utopia, but he discounts these as due to our relative inattention to the problem of control of human nature [by whom?] which he expects to be solved by our social sciences.[39] He seems to assume a relative neglect of the latter as the source of our evils. But it seems to me that since Bacon's day politics, economics, and ethics have received much more attention than physics. And the argument, that past social studies have not been sufficiently scientific, does not warrant the uncritical assumption that present social studies or any that we are likely to attain in the near future can be sufficiently advanced to solve our fundamental human difficulties. Such a degree of progress in science does not depend simply upon our willingness to follow one or another method. We are faced with insuperable difficulties. Moreover, when men do learn about the forces which control human nature the results are sometimes even more frightful. The psychology of persuasion as practiced by such eminently successful masters as Herr Hitler or Father Coughlin has shown that the constant and skillful repetition of demonstrable falsehoods is a far more effective way of influencing masses of men and women than any fair argument based on truth. These observations may be denounced as cynical, but any philosophy that ignores them smacks of the wisdom of the ostrich.

In his more sober moods Dewey is less optimistic, but still

[38] *Human Nature and Conduct*, p. 4.
[39] *Characters and Events* (ed. Ratner), p. 719.

insists on active effort as the only way. And he claims that such effort means something to the universe at large.[40] But that can hardly be established on an empirical basis. Nature seems quite indifferent to our human values. It gives us birth and sometimes joy, but also tragic disharmonies in our minds and bodies. In the end it kills all we love. It destroys in one moment all the work of the hard years. Poverty, disease, insanity, and abysmally stupid viciousness, prevail in all societies and mock man's pretension to be a god on earth. We cannot by thinking add a cubit unto our stature, nor even stop the progress of cancerous growths, of arterial sclerosis, or of senescence, much less the rotation of the earth. Knowledge does not always help us to control the future. We often foresee the inevitable without being able to stop it. It is not lack of courage but real wisdom to recognize our limitations in the face of the larger world of nature that is not of our own making. The theory that we know only what we create or make [41] would, if consistently carried out, deny any knowledge of the world and of those who brought us into it. We cannot create the world into which we come. Indeed if we could not be mere spectators to events beyond our control, neither Dewey nor anyone else could report evils without being responsible for what happened. In wiser moments Dewey, like James, recognizes that our vision extends beyond our manual reach or control, and that vision is itself an intense form of life.

Though Dewey himself is naturally interested in the analysis of general ideas such as the nature of the individual or the state, his distrust of universals makes him at times scorn all attempts to refine our "general concepts of institutions, individuality, state, freedom, law, order, progress, etc." [42] Especially does he turn his back on all discussions as to the nature of the *summum bonum* or ultimate good. He advocates instead concentration on the removal of specific evils. I think that this prevents him from formulating any adequate

[40] *Experience and Nature*, p. 420.   [41] *Op. cit.*, p. 428.
[42] *Reconstruction*, p. 193; *cf.* pp. 188, 190, 192.

theoretic guide, any Ariadne thread out of the labyrinthian mazes of experience which philosophy should offer if it is to be of any help in the analysis of diverse social problems. Impressed with the difference of opinion among philosophers in regard to abstract questions, he seems to think that we can get more agreement on specific issues.[43] This seems to me to ignore the intensity with which people do divide on specific social issues. If theorists do not agree (because in fact they do not want to), the disinclination comes from practical life rather than from pure theory. Moreover, we can get little help from the maxim that every situation must determine its own concrete good.[44] The world does not break itself up into a number of distinct atomic situations each with a determinate good. That which will remove some economic evil may bring about worse political ones, and vice versa. And we have no common unit to measure heterogeneous social values. This defeats the counsel to remove one evil at a time. Nor do we get very far by saying that what is good in any situation cannot be answered *a priori* but depends on actual conditions, if we have no guide as to the nature of the dependence.

In one phase of his thought, in his faith in progress, Dewey does attempt a general formula as to the *summum bonum,* and that is that growth is the only moral good. But, since all sorts of viciousness also grow and spread, this formula offers us no discriminating test. And what on this view *is* the moral end for those who are in homes for the incurable or are losing their means of support, their health, or are dying too slowly under helpless conditions? "Let us do the best we can," is meaningless, if we have no idea as to what *is* best or how it can be found.

It would be absurd to charge Dewey with being altogether insensitive to the values of enjoyment. But his writings do not seem to appreciate the classic values of solitude. His psychology is too behavioristic and social. He places too much

43 *Op. cit.,* p. 165.   44 *Op. cit.,* p. 163.

emphasis on being continually on the go, without regard to the places whereto it is worth while to go in order to stay rather than merely to pass through. This is analogous to the attitude which leads him to suppose that physical science has banished the idea of substance in developing the idea of function. In any case, against his view that rest and enjoyment are to be viewed as merely re-creational or instruments for further activity, I think we should recognize that they are ends in themselves and that life would not be worth anything without them. Contrary to his explicit denial, I should still maintain that many activities that are instrumental in enabling us to attain the things we enjoy, are still dreary and depressing. That indeed is the condition under which most men work in order to procure the things that make life worth while for themselves and their families. It does not prove anything to say that enjoyments, or, in his own terminology, "consummatory values," that are not also instrumental will turn to dust and ashes in our mouths.[45] All life and activity will also do that in the course of our mortality. Rest is no more merely a means to activity than peace is merely a means to war.

Throughout the ages, wise men have cultivated philosophical reflection regardless of its bearing upon the social struggle, not because they were cowardly or lazy members of a class of economic parasites, but because they recognize that in the pursuit of cosmic truth we are least subject to the uncertain turns of fortune and least likely to make others as well as ourselves suffer from the results of sowing vain hopes.

I must not conclude this ungracious task of devil's advocate without reiterating my profound conviction that in these days of morbid and deadly irrationalism John Dewey is rendering inestimable service in maintaining the liberal faith in enlightenment, based on free thought. But my criti-

[45] *Experience and Nature*, p. 365.

cism is not directed so much against his positive efforts as against incidental negations due to his unfortunate polemic against classical philosophy or to insufficient emphases on the things that are not in the center of his interests. The zeal which has actuated moralists and humanists aims at persuasion, at inducing others to join our church or party rather than to suspend judgment where the evidence is inadequate. Ardor for social reform is admirable in anyone, but detachment and a critical attitude are the special duties of those who as scientists or philosophers have to maintain the canons of intellectual integrity. Too often has devotion to temporal causes turned philosophical light into partisan heat. And Dewey surely agrees that we need to keep in mind the words of Emerson: He serves all who dares be true.

HEGEL'S RATIONALISM

O N THE CENTENARY of a philosopher's death we come not to re-bury or to praise him, but rather to better understand him, ourselves, and the world in which we live. If Hegel were dead it were best not to disturb his dust—to let the dead past bury its dead. Honest criticism is ruled out by the maxim *"De mortuis nihil nisi bonum,"* and conventional eulogy should be barred by the Talmudic warning that there is a day of judgment coming for the orator as well as for the deceased.

But in the realm of thought Hegel is not dead. He is still alive, perhaps too much so. His ideas dominate our evolutionary social sciences as well as most diverse schools of philosophy and theology. We can see this in the dialectic materialism of the orthodox Marxism which is disturbing the world, as well as in the Oxford idealism of our Anglo-American thought, which offers solace and support to the established order of spiritual values. Popular as well as radical philosophic thought seems to be ruled by his dogma that the abstract is unreal. Above all, Hegel still fashions our concepts of the history of social institutions, art, religion, and philosophy. Indeed, as to the history of philosophy his method of approach seems to be in almost exclusive possession of the field, though few recognize it as Hegelian in origin.

No one, I take it, denies that in the extent and depth of his insights Hegel is one of the great figures in the history of human thought, and that on many points in ethics, politics, art, religion, and the interpretation of human history, we can still learn much from him. Yet, it must also be admitted that, at least in our own country,[1] there has for the last thirty years been relatively little direct study of him, and that his

[1] Hibben's *Hegel's Logic* (1902) and Cunningham's *Thought and Reality in Hegel's System* (1910) seem to be our only extended studies of Hegel published this century.

influence has persisted only through the work of such expounders and independent assimilators as Green, Caird, Bosanquet, Bradley, Royce, and their idealist disciples. To promote a better understanding of Hegel, it is therefore not sufficient to pick out some one or other of his ideas and judge it according to its agreement or disagreement with our own present views. That is what he himself characterized as external reflection. If we wish to get at the heart of Hegel's life work, we must note his insistence, from the beginning to the end of his career,[2] that philosophic truth is identical with system and method.

If we ask Hegel himself for the distinctive traits of his philosophy, we find no pretense of offering us any new views of God, the physical world, human nature, knowledge, or duty. He does not regard himself as an innovator, but rather as one in a historical series of workers, trying to elaborate systematically the supreme truth that the real world is spiritual or mental. This according to Hegel is not only the view of all previous philosophers, but is involved in all human aspiration. The only claim he ever makes for himself is that of having adopted the true and definitive method for revealing or proving this ultimately spiritual nature of things.

It seems hardly questionable that Hegel regarded his logical or dialectic method as necessarily involved in what we call his metaphysical idealism or spiritualism. Not only is mind or spirit the highest definition of reality (the absolute), but thought (as philosophy) is the highest expression of spirit, so that the ultimate nature of things can be revealed only by rational thought. Hence his repeated assertion that the rational is real and the real is rational.

This insistence on the rational character of reality seems to justify the characterization of Hegel as a panlogist, which was made current by the acute and learned J. E. Erdmann.

[2] See the preface to the *Phenomenologie* (1807) and the second preface to the *Wissenschaft der Logik* (1831). *Cf.* also the concluding section of the *Logik* and of the first part of the *Encyklopädie*.

But it is highly instructive and characteristic of the dangers and difficulties in the understanding of Hegel that some of the most respect-inspiring of his recent expositors, like Kroner and N. Hartmann, have called him the greatest irrationalist in the history of human thought.[3]

The lover of irony may remark that this is in harmony with Hegel's identification of opposites. But though suggestive this observation can hardly be regarded as adequate. Common sense or the logic of the vulgar sciences may see in our paradox an illustration of the folly of the Hegelian method of drawing the implication of vague, undefined concepts, rather than the implication of definite propositions. But, in reply, it may well be urged that the method insists that truth is to be found not in concepts as such, but in their ultimate outcome.

Hartmann's contention, however, is in fact supported by cogent arguments that illumine the substance of Hegel's philosophy, though they do not seem to me to remove the ground for the traditional panlogistic, or rationalistic interpretation. It is true that the content of Hegel's philosophy, especially in the field of politics, art, and religion, is only outwardly constrained by the recurrent trinities of the dialectic form. But Hegel's insistent monism leaves no basis for any distinction between form and content. It is also true that the rational, which is the real according to him, is not merely finite human reason, but a metaphysical world-reason, divine and absolute. But "if mind is the absolute essence of all reality, individual mind and absolute mind are thereby identified," [4] and it is difficult to see how there can be anything really unknowable or irrational for human thought. We must grant Hartmann's point that Hegel's categories are not concerned with logical inference, but are rather of ontologic significance and sufficiently diverse and concrete to deal with living problems.

[3] R. Kroner, *Von Kant bis Hegel*, Vol. II, p. 271; N. Hartmann, *Hegel*, p. 15.

[4] Baillie, *Origin and Significance of Hegel's Logic*, p. 186.

Still, this does not deny the great importance which Hegel attaches to the logical transition from one category to another. Nor can we deny that in general the removal of logical contradiction is alleged as the motive power of the progress from one category to another. Hartmann finally contends that far from denying the existence of irrationality in the form of contradiction, Hegel finds it in all things, and the dialectic process does not remove it, but only places it in the absolute. This, however, cannot eliminate the fact that Hegel regards the process of reconciling contradictions as terminating in a reality which is completely rational and indeed is identical with rationality itself.

These brief considerations make it clear that we cannot adequately understand Hegel by labeling him either as a rationalist or as an irrationalist. We do not do justice to the content of his thought if we think of his system as so rationally concatenated that, once we grant *being*, we are bound by his ineluctable logic to follow him through the categories of being, essence, and concept, through the philosophy of nature, up to mind, subjective, objective, and absolute. Neither can we accept the view of those who, interested in the application of his views to some empirical issues of politics or history, completely disregard the idealistic system which is developed in his principal works, the *Phenomenologie* and the *Logik*, which underlies his philosophy of nature and largely molds, if it does not completely determine, his philosophy of right and his philosophy of mind. A sound interpretation must trace the conflicting motives of his rationalistic spiritualism and the empirical content which he tries to put into that system with the aid of his dialectic method. We can barely indicate the direction of such an interpretation by some comments on the three parts of his system, the logic, the philosophy of nature, and the philosophy of mind.

I

HEGEL'S LOGICAL SYSTEM can be called rationalistic if it is regarded either as a rigorous proof that ultimate reality is mind or idea, or as a description of the absolute world-process as a system or development.

The notion that the dialectic method has great logical cogency will not stand the test of rigorous scrutiny. The order in which the various categories succeed each other is at times highly arbitrary, and, in fact, varies in the various versions which Hegel has given us in the *Logik, Propaedeutic,* and *Encyklopädie,* without claiming any one of these to be *the* correct one. At its best, the claim for the dialectic is that it finds the assertion of an indispensable category, like *being,* involving us in contradictions, and that these contradictions are solved, removed, or absorbed by taking a higher category, like *becoming* or *determinate being.* Let us grant that this method is often illuminating. But the illumination depends in each case upon a fortunate discovery, and Hegel never offers proof that some other category than the one discovered would not answer the purpose as well. Without such proof there is an element of contingency in the order of the categories, e.g., when *cognition* follows *syllogism.* Many of the transitions are fantastic and supported only by verbal plays. A good deal of what he says about quantity and measure is definitely antiquated, and his attacks on Newton's calculus nothing more than perverse ingenuity.[5]

Related, but not identical with the view of the dialectic as a method of proof, is the view of it as a process of discovery or reconstruction. According to this view, the mind begins with the simplest object, to wit, *being,* and by thinking it finds or reconstructs the whole system which is its reality.

There are insuperable difficulties in viewing the dialectic as

[5] See W. R. Smith, *Lectures and Essays,* Vol. I, Chs. 2 and 5.

a process of finding the nature of reality. If the mind finds the world in this way, the world must be supposed to have existed before our finding it, and the order of thought in the process of discovery is not the order of the being that is thus found. This strikes a snag in Hegel's monistic refusal to distinguish between the order of thought and the order of being.

On the other hand, if by means of the dialectic the mind constructs reality, an insuperable difficulty arises as to the relation between the individual mind and the Absolute. Do we create the Absolute when we think it? Nor can we avoid difficulty by saying that every time we think the dialectic, the Absolute constructs or creates Himself according to the categories. What possible meaning can we assign to the word *creation* if we say that the Absolute creates Himself?

Nor is it more intelligible to say that the Absolute develops in time. Surely it is nonsense to say that first there was *being*, then *nothing*, then *quantity*, etc. All sorts of confusions arise because of Hegel's habitual use of metaphorical language. But it should be clear that he cannot mean in his dialectic to describe any merely temporal process or the way in which ordinary things do in fact change. He explicitly rejects what we today call evolution, that is, the transformation of organisms and species in time, and assures us that he is concerned with the concepts or ultimate categories of the Absolute. Now when he speaks of these categories negating themselves or reflecting on themselves, externalizing themselves or doing anything else, we cannot take him literally. Categories are not things changing in time. They are logical relations. Thus *being* and *nonbeing*, for instance, cannot combine to form *becoming*. For it is of the essence of the dialectic to show that neither can have any separate existence. They cannot therefore be literally said to combine. What the dialectic can or does claim is that both are only abstract phases of any process in which some determinate being changes into something else.

The method of showing this has been obscured for us by

the loose use of the word *contradiction* or *self-contradiction* where Hegel means opposition. Strictly speaking, only propositions, not categories, can contradict each other. What Hegel does show is that such statements as "the total reality is pure being" and "the total reality is nonbeing" are equally true.[6] For abstract being and nonbeing, taken by themselves, both exclude all determination and therefore cannot be distinguished from each other. They can be really distinguished only as phases of a process of *becoming*. But as such inseparable phases they are by no means entirely identical any more than one side of a street is identical with the other because the phrase *the other* necessarily involves and has no meaning apart from *the one*. It is therefore sheer carelessness to speak of the dialectic as involving the identity of opposites. Opposing things have identical elements, but opposition is not identity. The real situation is clearly enough revealed in Hegel's criticism of the laws of identity and contradiction. He points out, as is well known, that if we assert the identity of A with itself, our proposition involves some sort of distinction between the two A's identified. This is obviously true if A is any object whatsoever. For then its identity involves at least difference in time. This, however, does not mean that abstract identity and abstract difference are the same. It only means that they are always conjoined. Similarly Hegel points out that in the usual formulation of the principle of contradiction, nothing can be both A and not A, there is some element of identity between the A and the non-A—which again is obviously true if we speak as he and others do of "contradictory," i.e., opposing, things, qualities, or processes. Any dichotomous division into two mutually exclusive classes certainly involves some resemblance or element of identity between the two. But the respect in which two classes exclude

[6] I may barely refer to my own view that all statements about the absolute totality contain an element of indetermination, and therefore seemingly opposed statements may not be really contradictory. See pp. 16-18 *supra*.

each other is not the same as the one in which they are identical. This principle of the inseparable conjunction of opposing categories such as identity and difference, immediacy and mediation, and the like, I have ventured to call the principle of polarity.

To this principle no one has rendered greater service than Hegel: first, in the fruitful detection of opposing factors within seemingly simple entities or situations, and, secondly, in the subtle revelation of the inadequacy of treating one of two opposing factors as if it were absolutely independent. In this way we are saved from many false or inadequate alternatives. Also, all who wish to avoid the fallacy of reifying abstractions must agree with Hegel in denying them reality, i.e., if by reality we mean things in existence. But here a crude realism based on a prejudice in favor of existing things makes him deny the reality of abstractions in a way that deprives them of the validity which they have in their own domain. This element of crude realism shows itself in his demand that the ideal prove itself efficient in the temporal realm, in opposition to the Platonic and Kantian view that sees reality in ideal validities extending beyond any actual thing. There is an oscillation from this realism to a violently monistic idealism, which hastily insists that all opposition is overcome and is consequently so hostile to the distinctions of the understanding as to have drawn on Hegel the charge of being the prince of confusionists. Clearly there can be no real unity without real difference, no real synthesis without real elements. Only by continuous use of metaphor does he avoid the necessity of drawing a clear distinction between purely logical and temporal relations, between categories and things categorized. At times, however, he cannot avoid assuming this distinction, as, for example, when he insists that philosophy is interested in the changes of concepts rather than in the changes of nature.[7]

These difficulties are rooted in the metaphysical assumption that thought is the sole reality in which everything is in-

[7] *Encyklopädie*, Sec. 249.

[183]

volved, so that everything can be evolved from it. All that truly exists is rational and nothing is opaque to thought because everything is the outcome of the power of mind as thought.[8] Hegel's rationalism thus follows from the idealism which he inherits from Kant's deduction of the categories and Fichte's doctrine that the ego creates its own object or nonego.

Hegel's argument is put in its clearest form in the first section of the *Phenomenologie,* in which the deliverance of sense perception is acutely analyzed and its certainty shown to depend not on our passivity to external influence, but on the activity of our thought. Everything then is rational because everything is determined by the absolute mind whose real nature is self-conscious thought.

But it is not at all necessary that rationalism should logically follow from what in our modern perverse terminology we call idealism and what should more properly be called monistic mentalism or spiritualism. The example of Schopenhauer serves to remind us that such idealism can take a voluntaristic form and glory in irrationalism. And this suggests the horrible thought—horrible to Schopenhauer, to Hegel, and to their respective followers—that the difference between them on certain fundamentals is largely linguistic. After all, the proposition that everything is mental is one that no one, no matter how realistic, need reject if its proponent will admit, as every sane person does, that there is a real or genuine difference between the loaf of bread which I merely have in mind and the loaf of bread which I buy and use to satisfy the hunger of my wife and children. If this distinction is admitted the resolution to apply the term "mental" to both of these entities, ordinarily referred to as an imaginary and as a real loaf, is only a resolution as to the use of words. The realist can object only on the ground of linguistic policy, that nothing but confusion is gained by thus arbitrarily stretching

8 "Die wahrhafte Natur . . . ist . . . das *Erzeugnis meines Geistes* und zwar als denkenden Subjects," *Encyklopädie,* Sec. 23.

a word to cover the opposite of what we ordinarily and habitually suppose it to denote. If we decide to call everything that exists good then all evil things, like ignorance, suffering, and corruption, are good. But the difference between them and the rarer things we used to call good remains, in fact, what it was before, except for the solace which the new vocabulary offers. This solace perhaps constitutes a large part of the human value of philosophy. But like other human values, it is purchased at a cost, in this case, of debasing our intellectual currency and wiping out clear distinctions so as to dull the edge of righteous indignation against established abuses. So, in regard to Hegel's rationalism, the assertion that every real is rational and every rational real is either a mere resolution to use these words synonymously, or else an undue narrowing of the word *real* and a stretching of the word *rational* to include the irrational. Do we not thus seem to eliminate the irrational only by incorporating it into the essence of rationality itself? We can see this more concretely in Hegel's philosophy of nature and philosophy of mind.

II

UNLIKE his English followers, Hegel regarded his philosophy of nature as central to his system. This can be seen by its prominence in his logic.[9] How indeed can we have any systematic philosophy without an adequate account of the nature of the physical universe? We cannot reject the Hegelian physics without endangering his psychology, phenomenology, history, and other phases of objective mind which admittedly depend on physical factors. And if his method is completely rejected in the field of natural science, can we maintain it in the field of the humanistic sciences? But if we cannot reject

[9] See the Preface to the first edition of his *Logik* and the treatment of the category of *Objectivity*. Note also the frequency with which examples from physics are used to illustrate the meaning of almost all the categories.

his philosophy of nature without endangering his whole system, neither can we profitably dismiss it with the banal superficiality that the progress of science has left it behind. Heroic failures, the tragedies of intellectual adventure, are sometimes more instructive than petty successes. But as a fact, it is not true that the sterility of Hegel's philosophy of nature can be explained by the progress of science since his day.

It is a great mistake to suppose that Hegel was not much interested nor versed in natural science. Even in his pre-university days, his father procured him a private tutor in geometry and astronomy. As a theological student he took courses in anatomy and other sciences. And when he lectured at Jena he avidly pursued diverse courses in natural science and gave lectures on mathematics, as well as on *Naturphilosophie*. He qualified as a member of several societies of naturalists by his active interests in mineralogy, botany, and other fields. The result of these studies is seen on almost every page of the second part of the *Encyklopädie*, especially in the *Zusätze*. He had read the great masters of the different fields of physical science and the best authorities of his day—Kepler, Galileo, Newton, Lagrange, Berthollet, Bichat, Cuvier, *et al.*—and he brought a good deal of ingenuity to his task. Why then has his work in this field proved so utterly barren?

The answer seems to me to be found in his rationalistic method.

Hegel's primary interest, we must remember, was in the field of religion. He himself viewed his logic as giving us the successive attributes of the Absolute or God, arranged in order of concreteness. The God of his logic is the God before the creation of nature. His interest in nature is thus predominantly of the traditional theologico-anthropomorphic type.[10] His attempt therefore to explain nature in terms of

10 For Hegel's early speculations on physics see Nohl's *Hegels theologische Jugendschriften*, pp. 227 ff. and 371 ff., and Haering's *Hegel*, Vol. I, pp. 200 ff., 255, 378 ff., and 700 ff. Haering ignores the fact that the mechanical interpretation of nature is an integral part of the idealistic or Neo-Platonic physics of Kepler, Galileo, Leibniz, Newton, and Kant.

his logic is an attempt to follow the divine order in the creation of nature, and this point was justly regarded as central by his disciple and editor Michelet.

Without wishing to question the possibility of any mortal man being in possession of the secret of creation, it may be claimed that none of those who start from what they believe to be the divine idea of nature have thrown much light either on its details or on its general organization, and Hegel is no exception. The Copernican revolution and the general progress of modern mathematical and experimental methods in physics have really not affected him. He applies the old categories of teleology, of perfection and the like, to natural objects like the sun and the earth,[11] just as the scholastic philosophers did. The assumption that spirit creates nature does not help him to explain the nature of electricity, magnetism, and galvanism. Yet, these are precisely the topics that he deals with and must deal with if his philosophy of nature is to have any content. To be sure, he does rail against Schelling and others who try to deduce the facts of nature from *a priori* considerations.[12] But not all who denounce crime are themselves innocent. Certainly he does try to remove the contingency of such facts as that there are seven planets, four (*sic*) elements, three continents: Africa, Europe, and Asia (America and Australia do not count), or that there are three senses (the five are reduced to three). He does it by giving them a dialectic derivation in the Procrustean form of thesis, antithesis, and synthesis.[13]

Now these are not mere lapses. They characterize his treat-

[11] "Die Erde ist unter allen Planeten die vortrefflichste," etc., *Werke*, Vol. VII, p. 432.

[12] For Schelling's criticism of Hegel's philosophy of nature see the appendix to Meyerson's *De l'explication dans les sciences,* and Dilthey's *Schriften*, Vol. IV, p. 275.

[13] *De Orbitis Planetarum* and the *Zusatz* to Sec. 270 of the *Encyklopädie* (*Werke,* Vol. VII, pp. 120-124), Secs. 281-285, Sec. 339 *Zusatz,* Sec. 358. The philosophy of nature does not need experience (or individual facts) for its final justification, *Werke,* Vol. VII, p. 18.

ment of every topic and follow from his essential and fundamental assumption that thought is the one great reality in
which everything else is involved, so that everything else can
be evolved from it. This is fundamental not only to Hegel,
but to the great tradition of which he is the culmination.
Circumspect and cautious as is the critical Kant, the latter's
doctrine that the laws of nature are created by the categories
of the understanding is connected with the belief that we have
a priori knowledge that nature follows Euclidean geometry
and Newtonian mechanics. And so long as these truths are
regarded as necessary, they cannot be derived from experience.
But if we know *a priori* that geometric and mechanical laws
govern nature, why not *a priori* knowledge of electric, mechanical, and biologic laws? That is precisely the essence of
the romantic *Naturphilosophie*. And Hegel, believing in the
primacy and omnipotence of spirit, thinks of nature as its
product. Of course, even an arch-romantic, like Schelling, admits that the self-consciousness which creates nature is the
transcendental and not the empirical self. But the two are
continuous, and all that is said about the transcendental self
is in fact based on what we know of our empirical consciousness, so that the romantic philosophy of nature cannot escape
anthropomorphism. Its rationalism is thus romantic in the
sense that it enthrones human willfulness as the creator of
nature. Hegel's *Naturphilosophie* proved itself much more
sterile than that of Schelling precisely because it was much
more rationalistic in relying on supposed *a priori* ideas rather
than on the intuitions of genius. Schelling in some cases
proved suggestive and stimulated research; Hegel defended
ancient errors with perverse ingenuity.

In theologic language, this may be put thus: the thought
which creates nature is God's thought, not our frail human
thought. Do we know God's thought through and through?
Hegel's philosophy not only assumes it and insists on it, but
pretends to give us a formula for the necessary laws according
to which it must operate. If then his logic does not explain

the contingent facts of nature, it fails to give us a concrete universal. This, in fact, he himself realizes when he admits that there are contingent facts in nature which cannot be derived from the idea. But with characteristic complacency or intellectual arrogance he puts the blame not on his method or assumptions, but on the facts of nature. Nature is not sufficiently strong or rational to conform to our concept of it.

Hegel's philosophy of nature pretends to go beyond the empirical and mathematical results of natural science to deal with the idea of nature. But what is this idea? If we mean by it something that exists only in human thoughts, then since these thoughts, as temporal events, are connected with human bodies, ideas are only parts of nature. Our idea of the solar system is a psychologic product, the history of which belongs to the biography of various individuals and to the history of science, while the history of the solar system goes much farther back in time. If, however, Hegel uses the word *idea* (as he does) in the Platonic sense, as the form, or system, of nature itself, then so long as actual knowledge is capable of growth it can never be said to be adequate or equal to its object. The idea of nature then remains a formal or regulative ideal to guide or direct the process of increasing knowledge, but does not assure us knowledge of nature's substantial content. A philosophy of nature, therefore, must either be concerned with questions of pure logic, or else with existential propositions of physics, which never rise above the realm of probability. Now, though Hegel is aware that philosophy must depend in some way on empirical material, his rationalism will not allow him to recognize that a philosophy of nature must deal with probabilities. And his monism will not allow him to recognize the distinction between formal and material considerations as to nature.

The limitation of Hegel's rationalism becomes clearer when we contrast it with that of Galileo, Kepler, and Newton. These founders of modern science can also be called rationalists. In line with the Platonic tradition in which they were brought up, they assumed that the book of nature was written in simple mathematical or geometric patterns. But they had the good sense of spiritual humility. They realized that to study the book of nature men must begin with the simplest elements and study their invariant relations. The mechanical interpretation of nature is a product of this genuinely idealistic faith, that is, faith in universal laws which give a constant form to the changes of nature. The development of modern mathematical physics, such as the theory of relativity and statistical mechanics, and our greater insight into the nature of pure mathematics, show us more clearly the abstract form of these universal laws or forms of natural change. But we cannot deduce the concrete reality of natural fact from pure abstractions. Always there is the element of contingency, brute matter or ὕλη. And if we deny the latter, our abstract forms collapse into nothingness. On the other hand, the failure of Hegel's *Naturphilosophie* does not justify the ideaphobia or misology of so-called scientific empiricism. For no *progress* in any field of science is possible without some assumption of greater rationality than we have at any point of time actually achieved.

III

WHILE HEGEL'S THOUGHT has proved barren in the field of natural philosophy, it has had an enormous influence in the humanistic field. Shall we attribute this to the accident that some of his ideas have found favorable soil, or is there some one phase of his thought that has proved peculiarly fruitful? While the triune form of the dialectic is kept, it here becomes at times little more than a mannerism, which seems in no way to prevent him from expressing his very decided opinions, some of which have the penetration of genius and others of which are decidedly partisan, provincial, illiberal, and sectarian. If any example be needed, we may mention the grounds on which he favors war and disparages Kant's noble ideal of perpetual peace founded on a world federation of republics (i.e., commonwealths governed by law), or the grounds on which he condemns Fries' appeal for popular participation in government, his bigoted polemics against Catholicism, or the way he glorifies preference for Gothic art into an absolute. Any method which proves so many disputable propositions is rightly suspect.

There are, however, those who insist that Hegel's whole logic is really the logic of the *Geisteswissenschaften,* as opposed to the logic of the *Naturwissenschaften.* This assumes that thought about human psychology, history, politics, art, or religious institutions, follows a logic different from that which concerns itself with natural objects. Such an assumption seems to me indefensible historically and logically, as well as inconsistent with all that Hegel says in his *Logik,* where illustrations from natural science abound. But, waiving this point, we may ask—What method, if any, has Hegel introduced into the mental and social sciences? The followers of Marx and others make a good deal of the dialectic as emphasizing inevitable opposition, or struggle, in the process of social change. But no one can well deny that wherever Hegel refers to strife and opposition he feels obliged to bring in some synthesis. This emphasis on the interdependence of conflicting factors is now generally called the organic point of view, as opposed to the rationalistic or mechanical view, which is willing to trace the effects of abstract factors in their separation. Religion and laws, for instance, should be viewed not as artificially instituted, but as integral to and expressive of the life of a people. Though this is an old view, admirably applied by men like Montesquieu, there can be no doubt that Hegel gave great impetus to this method of approach. Thus Feuerbach integrated religion in anthropology, and other Hegelians, Vatke, Strauss, and C. Bauer, made it possible to view the religion of the Old and New Testaments as historic evolutions. But this organic method as developed by Hegel is an unstable concept and oscillates between crude realism and abstract rationalism. Emphasis on historic setting and continuity with the past has in him, as in Savigny and in others, discouraged ethical idealism and made for an historical relativism which led to the idolatry of the actual. But the inherent absolutism of his thought asserts itself in taking the political element of life, the State, and setting it up as the Absolute, the God on earth, to the neglect of individual and international rights. The same tendency to abstract rationalism shows itself even more clearly in the attempt to write history in terms of periods which succeed each other according to a linear series of abstract ideas, connected with each other by a decidedly abstract and mechanistic logic, without regard to the variations of individual men and their peculiar geniuses. Here again, his failure to distinguish between formal and material considerations, and his unwillingness to be satisfied with the most probable results, make a real synthesis impossible and make him oscillate between crude realism and abstract rationalism.

Let us look at this somewhat more closely.

In his ethics Hegel opposes abstract individualism and the absolute value that Kant set on the morality of conscience. For the good will has worth only if it is directed to a rational end from which can be deduced actual duties and positive lines of conduct. In the ethics of the family Hegel refuses to consider such empirical biological facts as the approximate equality of the number of men and of women. But in opposing the contractual view of marriage and the importance of romantic love he depends on the empirical psychological argument that mutual affection is more securely based on living together wisely.

In the field of jurisprudence, Hegel's rationalism clings to concepts that do not advance the analysis of actual problems. This is true of his theory that property is the realization of the will or of freedom of personality. As my property right in any object necessarily limits the rights and freedom of everyone else, the real problems of the law of property are not adequately met by the notion of freedom alone. We need some theory as to how this freedom is to be properly limited, and this Hegel does not offer because of insufficient attention to the empirical content of law. Similarly, there is a verbal nobility to his theory that punishment carries into effect the will of the criminal, but it throws no light on what punishment is the suitable one in any given case, nor what offenses should be treated with the mercy of the pardoning power, nor how society is to defend itself against dangerous aggression by those who defy its laws.

Hegel's main attention, however, is devoted to the state, on which he lavishes all the honorific phrases at his bestowal. In a sense he may be said to have tried to revive the Aristotelian or Hellenic conception of the state as the organized life of culture. But though he rejects Hobbes' notion that the state rests on force or serves empirical human needs he is extreme in his emphasis on the need of security and on a unitary sovereign in the person of a hereditary monarch.

According to him, each national state is absolute and war is not only necessary but a spiritual good. Since ethics is embodied in the state and there is no sovereign over all states, they are in relation to each in "a state of nature" not subject to genuine moral laws. They are not, for instance, obliged to keep their agreements. From this anarchic and amoralistic view of international relations Hegel tries to escape by regarding history as the court in which Providence passes judgment on the various nations. This makes history a theodicy; but it also makes mere survival the test of national righteousness—a doctrine that misses the tragedy of history and is equivalent to Napoleon's dictum that God is on the side of the heaviest artillery. This phase of Hegel's doctrine, however, is covered by the use of logical instead of theological terms, by an attempt to show that development in time follows the order of the categories of logic. But, as the number of categories is finite, history completes itself in the Prussia of his day. Moreover to display this logical order one people and only one can at any time represent the world spirit; the rest are negligible and have no rights.

What does Hegel's rationalism mean in the realm of history? Let us consider it first in the domain with which we are all presumably more or less familiar, namely, in the history of philosophy. No one can read the pre-Hegelian histories of philosophy, such as those of Brucker, Buhle, or Tennemann, without feeling a lack of general significance. They give us only the lives and opinions of diverse philosophers in chronologic order, which rationally seems hardly more significant than the alphabetic order. But Hegel for the first time gives us a coherent history of philosophy itself. In it there seems nothing contingent or accidental. The time-order as well as the content of the different philosophies seems dictated by some logical order (though not necessarily that of the categories in the *Science of Logic*). Every philosophy is viewed as a development of or an antithesis (now called reaction) to the previous one. This has brought about an almost complete revolution in our subject matter. Indeed, I know of no other single book that has so completely revolutionized a field of human study. The massive philologic equipment of Zeller, the imposing if somewhat superficial historic learning of Kuno Fischer, and the ingenious schematism of Erdmann and Windelband, are all dominated by the Hegelian conception and seem to have fixed it as the canonical view of the history of philosophy.

And yet without wishing to return to the former blind and insipid empiricism, or to ignore the great wealth of insight which the Hegelian method has brought us, we may well deny that the contingent or accidental element has really been, or can be, eliminated from the history of philosophy. No one has in fact ever shown any logical necessity why Parmenides, Plato, and Aristotle should have appeared and thought as they did, or why they should have been followed by such men as Zeno and Epicurus, and these by still smaller men, until suddenly the great figure of Plotinus rises from the Egyptian sands. Why, when the absolute attained complete self-consciousness in the philosophy of Hegel, did his followers divide into such discordant groups? His method really assumes that the latest in time is the fullest and nearest to perfection. But if chronology were the test of truth the materialistic Feuerbach or Karl Marx would be an improvement on the idealistic Hegel. In point of fact, however, Hegel's philosophy of mathematics cannot be compared favorably with that of his despised contemporary Fries, or even with that of his predecessor Kant. No! Men and their idiosyncrasies, the inexplicable but powerful idiosyncrasies of genius, cannot be eliminated from the history of philosophy any more than individual genius can be eliminated from the history of poetry or any other art. It is generally easy to explain events after they have happened. For our explanations can seldom be checked by experimental verification, and so are in fact not challenged. Any explanation which seems plausible *a priori* can hold the field. But to impose a completely logical or rational order on the history of philosophy is to do violence to the obvious facts in history. If individual men with their inexplicable individual peculiarities are ignored, what is left is not the history of the actual concrete reality but at best an abstract phase of it. This abstract phase is illuminating and important, but it cannot be recognized except as abstract. Those who believe in the reality of abstract universals may be pardoned a bit of ironic glee in seeing what little there is left of Hegel's *concrete* universal in the field of the history of philosophy.

If in the history of art, religion, and philosophy, Hegel sins by leaving out individual men and their inexplicable traits, he sins even more grievously in the philosophy of history by identifying the universal absolute spirit with local contingencies such as the Prussian monarchy. Why must the absolute, as Hegel insists, incarnate himself in only one nation at a time so that others have no rights against it? Why should monarchy, even if the monarch lacks wisdom and good will, be the embodiment of eternal reason? Hegel naïvely asserts that Frederick II was the first sovereign who kept the general interests of the state steadily in view—which unduly flattering judgment of Frederick can certainly not be an argument for the absolute rationality of monarchy. Why must the absolute reason express itself in the acts of government-appointed officials rather than in the deliberation of popularly chosen representatives? There may be empirical wisdom in preferring one to the other under certain conditions, but the totality of such conditions of human life is never fully known to us. Hence it is dangerous for a philosopher to speak in the name of the Absolute on such matters as the English reform bill, on which history has mocked Hegel's analysis and predictions. This again is saying that in the field of spirit as in the field of nature he makes no room for the weighing of probabilities. Where everything is the manifestation of the Absolute the weighing of probabilities by applying mathematics to hypotheses that have no support except harmony with past experience is out of the question; yet that is the best wisdom that imperfect man can achieve.

IV

HISTORICALLY Hegel's philosophy may be viewed as a synthesis of the romantic movement which had its sources in Protestantism, Rousseau, Kant, Fichte, and Schelling, and of the rationalism of the eighteenth century which had its roots in classical antiquity, of which Hegel was always a keen student. His bureaucratic antecedents and temper made him emphasize the values of order and renew the Aristotelian conception of the state in a somewhat non-Hellenic and illiberal way. But his fundamental logic is essentially romantic in the sense that the cosmic order is conceived of in an anthropomorphic manner subservient to the accidents of human volition. Classic wisdom as well as more ancient religion demand discipline of spirit and the recognition of a cosmic order greater than that which we can create or even completely understand. Hegel is one of the most significant figures in philosophy because he faced this dilemma of the human spirit, how to find a *via media* between romanticism and rationalism, between capricious anarchy and despotism. But the history of his immediate followers shows that he did not adequately solve his problem.

Hegel was profoundly impressed with the Heraclitean flux. More than any other philosopher since Heraclitus he realized the element of strife or opposition within the flux, but his monistic absolute idealism made him too ready and hasty to find solutions or reconciliations. At times he recognizes the reality of opposition and insists that it is not removed when two opposites are seen to be parts or phases of a larger unity. But his traditional loyalties defeat this realistic vision and he does all too frequently speak as if formal unity wipes out conflict and disharmony. But the fact that two opponents are at each other's throats, which they could not be if they were entirely separated, does not elevate their struggle to a higher unity. The word *higher* is here as almost anywhere else a snare and a delusion covering the absence of meaning with a vague afflatus. In fact, the unity of opposites is just another name for the brute fact that there is real opposition. Multiplicity and struggle, finitude and evil, contingency and imperfection, are as primary or real as anything else, and cannot be rationally deduced from or wiped out by any monistic absolute idea. The aphorism that the real is rational and that the rational is real either rests on arbitrary definitions of real and rational or else it is a philosophically fatal falsehood. Unfortunately it satisfies human vanity and persists by perpetually shifting from one meaning to another. Philosophy always has been and must continue to be a search for a rational order in the chaos of empirical happenings. And Hegel has rendered great service in showing the untenability and self-contradiction of pure empiricism. But rationalism can succeed only by being humble and recognizing its own difficulties or limitations. It must admit that rational order is only one phase of a world which always contains more than we can possibly explain. Intellectual arrogance is a spiritual blindness fatal to the life of true philosophy.

BELIEF

Because of its intimate relation to conduct, belief has been of continuing interest to social philosophers and its psychological nature a frequent subject of study. An important modern analysis of belief was that of Hume, who viewed it as a psychologic state differing from imagination only by its greater vividness and steadiness. It is at present generally recognized that to the extent that an idea fills the mind to the exclusion of possible alternatives we tend to hold it true. Thus fixed ideas and inflexible beliefs arise in a state of mental debility. Certain recent psychologists emphasize, as did the patristic and scholastic writers, the active element of assent in the judgment that something is true. Romantic philosophers have stressed the purely voluntary character of this assent; while others insist that when we truly believe, as when we truly love, we feel compelled to do so. The recognition that we have a choice means that another view is possible, and the entertaining of this possibility may be called an implicit doubt. One may, however, distinguish between the compulsion of the evidence of the subject matter and the inner compulsion of one's own nature to hold a proposition true despite the absence of objective evidence sufficient to silence the doubt of others. From this point of view beliefs differ in degree of intensity, indicated by such phrases as "it is my opinion," "I am persuaded," "I am unalterably convinced."

Whatever the psychological characteristics of belief, it is clear that its specific forms are largely social in origin and are in many cases conditioned by our habitual emotional reactions, with the result that through following a certain mode of life one generally ends by sharing the beliefs of others who follow that mode. Hypocrites are scarce because it is so easy to believe that which our conduct professes. Men generally believe that their professional groups, their nation, their city or section of the country, their college or fraternity, have certain inherent superiorities wholly invisible to outsiders. The social determination of belief is even more evident in such phenomena as booms, panics, crazes, or fads. Le Bon has pointed out that in a crowd the beliefs or opinions of the wiser members are generally depressed to the level of the majority. For the power of suggestion increases rapidly with an increase in numbers, and it is always difficult to maintain opinions or practices different from those professed and approved by one's associates. Heretics who defy the opinions of the multitude depend all the more intensely on the devotion of their supporters.

Beliefs are transmitted not only unconsciously but also through the direct and intentional pressure of parents, teachers, or other authoritative leaders. Both types of transmission are most effective in small homogeneous communities. It seldom occurs to a member of such a group even to doubt its prevailing views. The processes of intercommunication, commerce, travel, or the mixing of diverse peoples in large cities break down such primitive certainty. "To have doubted one's own first principles is the sign of a civilized man," Mr. Justice Holmes has said. The state of doubt is, however, difficult and unpleasant. Doubt, "where all is double," requires much free intellectual energy. It complicates and renders more difficult our practical choices. To rid themselves of this burden most people rely on natural leaders and authorities or cling resolutely to certain plausibilities. Some attempt to follow the method of science, questioning everything until doubt is no longer possible; but since action must often precede the acquisition of adequate knowledge a large number of practical beliefs cannot be based on scientific evidence. Many firmly held beliefs are positively irrational and rest on excessive credulity or obstinate pride of opinion. Such beliefs are of the essence of superstition. The tendency to regard any chance coincidence of two events as a case of causal connection has not only led to various primitive, magical ideas, such as those attributing disease to the evil eye, but continues to add to the modern fund of superstitions. Persisting legends or myths, such as those glorifying certain statesmen as free from human imperfections, testify to man's perennial credulity, his will to believe that which is simple and pleasant.

Philosophers have long differed as to the way in which beliefs influence social evolution. Deterministic theories minimize their importance; beliefs are said to be only the ideologic reflections of the physical environment, of the racial inheritance, of the system of production, of the interests of the dominant class, or of irrational emotions and feelings. On the other hand men have commonly believed in indoctrinating children and adults with the proper beliefs, whether by education, propaganda, preaching, advertising or various more indirect methods. In recent years, with the growth of psychologic interpretations of social development, the role of beliefs has been increasingly emphasized. The widespread recognition that the belief in science and the scientific method has revolutionized modern life is accompanied by the assertion that other types of belief have been equally or even more effective.

It is an ancient view, shared by such writers as Plutarch and Machiavelli, that religious and even superstitious beliefs are necessary for social life, "to manage and reform the vulgar." This idea appears in a modern sophisticated version in the theory of Sorel and Ross that myths or illusory beliefs are necessary to give *élan* and direction to social movements. These theorists have failed, however, to show by analysis what kinds of myths are effective, for obviously not all myths are influential. Again it has been held, notably by Kidd, that rational beliefs are always individualistic, and that socially desirable conduct requires the subordination of the individual to the interests of the race, a process which can be sanctioned only by supernatural religion. This theory shows traces of the old view that religious peoples are the strongest. Doubts as to the complete social value of religious beliefs arise, however, from a survey of such facts as the religious sanctions of celibacy, slavery, the caste system or the sacrifice of children to Moloch; they arise even more strongly from a study of the extermination of such groups as the Albigenses and the Waldenses, because of the tenacity of their religious beliefs, and of the serious retardation of others by religious wars. The supposed facts about primitive life, assembled by Frazer to prove that superstitious and magical beliefs have strengthened respect for government, for life and property, for marriage and sexual morality, and have thus made for greater security, can be offset by an equally long list of the horrible effects on social life of various magical beliefs and superstitions.

More convincing is Max Weber's theory of the importance of religious ideas in molding economic development, and specifically his attempt to show that protestant asceticism led to the development of modern capitalism, although many of its underlying assertions have been successfully challenged, notably by L. Brentano, and although Weber has not made out a case for direct causal relation. The ambitious effort of Durkheim and his school to show that "the fundamental categories of thought and consequently of science are of religious order" is based upon a view of religion which makes it synonymous with all the ritual of social life. But the fact that people take part in a common ritual or cult does not always mean that they have a common belief. Here too there is insufficient evidence of a definite causal relation between belief and the course of social evolution.

It is nevertheless true that most societies have felt the acceptance of certain beliefs essential to their survival, and have attempted by various means to suppress the practice and spread of other beliefs. In closely knit communities departures from group standards are so rare as to cause little concern. Few, if any, peoples previous to the Greeks thought it necessary to formulate the beliefs underlying their religion or their family, clan or industrial organization. While certain expressions were regarded as endangering the community because they might bring down the wrath of the gods or of evil spirits, speculation itself was considered too unimportant to require suppression. It is when religious organizations become voluntary and a definite formula of belief for admission to a group is necessary that dogma and creed appear. And it is when a society includes many different elements that the nonacceptance of certain beliefs first becomes a problem. Thus there is no creed or dogma in the Old Testament. The early development of the Christian Church in the midst of hostile religions and its subsequent incorporation of so many diverse national groups and practices led to its insistence on the suppression of heresy. Unity of dogma was all the more urgent when the Roman Empire fell and the Catholic Church tried to continue to rule different provinces subject to different temporal powers. Having assured the acceptance of its great central beliefs, the Catholic Church has since allowed a great diversity of opinion and practice among its members; but the importance assigned to belief by the Christian tradition has continued to influence the history of the western world.

Political considerations have often led temporal rulers to support religious beliefs, while regard for public order and tranquillity have been the basis of many persecutions of heretics. The gradual secularization of thought and the more complete separation of church and state have led to a decreasing interest on the part of political rulers in religious beliefs and a consequent removal of religious disabilities. In England commercial expansion and the growth of dissent in the middle classes and in the cities led to the Toleration Act of 1689 and later to the emancipation of Catholics and Jews, the removal of religious tests for holding property or public office. One of the last steps in this direction occurred in 1877 when the English universities ceased to require adherence to the Thirty-Nine Articles as a prerequisite for fellowships and other privileges.

But with the growth of religious tolerance economic, political and social beliefs have assumed a greater importance and have become the subject of increasing attempts at control by governments or by voluntary associations. Modern governments, regarding socialism as a danger, have disqualified its adherents from certain honors, dignities, or offices. It is often alleged that American universities adopt similar methods. Certainly belief in a heterodox code of marital or sexual relations might prevent a man from being elected to public office in some parts of the United States or in Great Britain. The United States excludes immigrants who believe in philosophic anarchy, and it excludes from admission to citizenship those who believe that the law of God or conscience may take precedence over the call of the state to bear arms. After the First World War an attempt was made in New York State to bar from teaching in the public schools those who did not believe in the existing form of national or state government. Similar attempts to prevent the dissemination of certain beliefs have been made in most modern states; while under dictatorships both the control of the expression of opinion and the development of methods of fostering beliefs approved by the ruling group have reached a high degree of perfection. In revolutionary movements as well, such as the socialist or communist parties, the need is strongly felt for formulated creeds to which adherents must subscribe so that heretics may be removed. Toleration of beliefs contrary to those one cherishes is possible only where there is a certain security and only for those who care more for scientific rectitude in the search for truth than for any of its results.

CROCE AND VICO

PATRIOTISM has led Italians to devote a great deal of attention to Vico; and the diverse schools of Italian thought,
positivists, Hegelians, and adherents of the national Italian
school, all claim Vico as their own, indulging in consequent
controversies as to the proper way of interpreting him. Vico
readily lends himself to such controversies because his was
essentially an autodidactic, eclectic, and unsystematic mind,
so that everyone may pick out what he likes and interpret
the rest to suit himself. (That this is not an unfounded statement, everyone can verify by reading Vico's catalogue of what
his New Science is.) [1] Croce's book,[2] however, is delightfully
free from controversy and that philologic straining to produce
the appearance of consistency which makes so many works on
Vico, as on Kant, resemble in method the old-fashioned textbooks of gospel harmony. Instead of an apology, or, what is
now so fashionable, an attempt at an "objective" historical
account of his author's thought, Croce boldly starts out to
give us a philosophical evaluation, i.e., an exposition of Vico
that should distinguish between the true and the false.

Croce characterizes his attitude to Vico as that of a warm
lover but not a blind one (pp. 42-43). Opposed to those who
grow enthusiastic and write defenses, "some minds are self-
willed and suspicious, quick to mark any trifling contradiction, merciless in demanding proof of every statement,
and indefatigable in wielding the forceps of dilemma to dis-
member an unfortunate great man" (p. 42). But such dismem-
berment generally proves vain. The insight or spirit of the
great man remains significant. If we had to choose between
these two attitudes of faith and distrust, it would be better

1 *Scienza Nuova* (2d ed.), Book II, Ch. II, Sec. 2.
2 Benedetto Croce, *La Filosofia di Giambattista Vico* (1911). Translated
by R. G. Collingwood under the title, *The Philosophy of Giovanni
Battista Vico* (The Macmillan Company, New York, 1913).

to prefer the former which "may yet enrich us by one or two aspects of the truth," while the attitude of distrust leaves us without any gain in insight. But the proper attitude, the critical one, is neither of these. It interprets freely but not fancifully, not ignoring the letter but transcending it to attain the spirit.

Croce's method, of course, involves setting up the critic's own standpoint as the test of truth. But can the "objective" historian really dodge the responsibility for a philosophic standpoint of his own from which to judge the philosophic importance of the propositions he examines? If the critic's own philosophy acts as a disturbing medium, this can be determined only by establishing a better medium, not by supposing that a philosophy can be viewed without the medium of the interpreter's own ideas.

From Croce's point of view (a modified Hegelian pantheism), the truth of Vico's system is the idealistic pantheism which worked itself out in Vico's mind in spite of the latter's devotion to Catholic theism. The great service of Vico is, thus, to have seen history and the institutions of culture as revelations of the eternal forms of the human mind—though this vision was obscured and confused by his determination to be and remain an orthodox Catholic. Hence Croce's exposition is a continuous effort to separate the grain from the dross, without any effort to hide the dross.

Croce's exposition, like Vico's own books, is singularly devoid of the sense for system which is often supposed to be the very essence of philosophy. Students brought up on the classical division of philosophical problems into logical, metaphysical, psychological, etc., may well object that Croce draws no clear line between philosophy and the empirical material, like Greek and Roman history, theories of mythology, etc., which occupies more than half of the book. This is not an altogether trivial point, for if we press Croce along this line we come to real obscurity in his fundamental views concerning the relation of the empirical to the *a priori* or eternal, which, he often assures us, is the only object of philosophy. What, for instance, are the eternal forms of mind which underlie the historical process? The clearest answer to this is in the statement of the philosophic significance of Vico's law of "reflux": "The mind after traversing its course of progress, after rising from sensation successively to the imaginative and the rational universal and from violence to equity, is bound in conformity with its eternal nature to re-traverse the course, relapse into violence and sensation, and thence to renew its upward movement, to commence a reflux" (p. 122). But nowhere, in this book, does Croce tell us whether sensation and the imaginative and the rational universals are three categories of empirical psychology or ontologic stages of a mind or World Process. He rejects Vico's assertion that the types of culture represented in the different stages of Greek and Roman civilization must forever repeat themselves, "even if infinite worlds were produced from time to time through eternity." Croce sees no necessity why those empirical facts should repeat themselves; but why must the passage from violence to equity, or from sensation to the rational universal, forever repeat itself? The absence of an adequate discussion of the metaphysics which must underlie the New Science, and of any criterion by which to distinguish the empirical from the "eternal" in history, leaves this whole matter essentially obscure.

Croce insists that Vico's great *forte* is his speculative insight and that the basic principle of this insight is to be found in his theory of knowledge, viz., in the principle that we can truly know only that which we have created. This peculiar adaptation of the traditional maxim that philosophy consists of the knowledge of the causes of things, Croce regards as the fundamental principle of all modern idealistic systems and of all true philosophy, and Vico's originality in formulating and adopting this principle is defended with considerable ardor. The consequences drawn from this are: That the social world, being the creation of man, is best known, that physics, dealing with matter not created by man, must always be beyond his demonstrative knowledge (though he may have opinions rising to certitude), and that mathematical knowledge, while demonstrative, is futile because it does not create reality. It does not occur to Croce that these consequences might be regarded as the very *reductio ad absurdum* of the principle which he thinks so important. It would seem hardly necessary at this date to defend the existence of a genuine science of physics, or the assertion that our physics is at least as developed as our social science; but even the conclusion with regard to mathematics, though occasionally heard to this day, is demonstrably false, as the slightest familiarity with the progress of physics in the works of Archimedes, Galileo, Huyghens, or Newton will amply illustrate.[3] That Vico should have believed so, is readily understood when we remember that he was a professor of rhetoric and poetry, that, according to his own autobiography,[4] his knowledge of geometry did not extend beyond Euclid's *pons asinorum*, and that he would not read any works on experimental physics because such works can have no bearing on philosophy and are written in such barbarous style. But that anyone should follow him today when the mathematical ideas of Maxwell and Willard Gibbs have transformed our modern physics, seems to me incomprehensible.

The truth seems to be that the effort to magnify the im-

[3] One is led to similar reflections by Gentile's conception of truth as "Pure Act." The motive of Gentile's idealism seems to me rightly grasped when it is contrasted with Bradley's conception of the coherency of all experience as the test of truth. That test makes truth a transcendent ideal never completely attainable. Hence Gentile's effort to find in the pure act of the spirit an immanent truth. But what is this pure act of the spirit? The moment we say anything about it we treat it as an object, and belie Gentile's fundamental assumption that the pure act is prior to all distinction between subject and object. If the pure act creates everything, how is it to be distinguished from the orthodox conception of a creating God? Or does the pure act create God as well as nonbeing? Gentile has not overcome the difficulties with which Schelling grappled far more resolutely.

[4] See *Oeuvres choisies*, tr. Michelet, I, pp. 15-16, 23-24.

portance of Vico by representing him as a precursor of Croce's own speculative metaphysics, does not do Vico as much justice as do some of the more positivistic interpretations, e.g., Cosentini's. When one reads the *Scienza Nuova* nowadays, and even in Croce's own estimation, what makes Vico's theory of human culture so significant is that in an age of mechanical theories of life, when language, mythology, religion, and political institutions were treated as inventions due to clever men or to a deus ex machina, Vico approached all these problems from what is now called the organic point of view, i.e., viewed social institutions as growths rather than as inventions or creations, and in an age of mechanical individualism (typified by the social contract theory), he approached the problems of civilization from the point of view of a social psychology that allowed room for divergences of modes of feeling and thought undreamed of by his contemporaries. (It may be remarked, in passing, that the concept of the social organism in positivistic literature is precisely that of Vico's Providence, which makes the social world "the issue of an intelligence which often diverges, is sometimes contrary, and always superior to the particular ends which men set themselves.") [5] It is well to note that when Vico comes to formulate his own criterion of truth he does not use the principle of the convertibility of the true and the created, but rather the older principle of Catholic authority: "Whatever the whole or a plurality of mankind feel to be just should serve as a rule of social action." [6] In accordance with this criterion, the belief in Providence, in the sanctity of human marriage, and reverence for the dead are found to be universal and made the basis of his teaching. This is not a detached statement or episode, but as the subtitle of the *Nuova Scienza* indicates, the whole motive of the work as an effort to found a system of jurisprudence on the common beliefs and nature of man. It is only Croce's indifference to the philosophy of

[5] *Scienza Nuova*, Book V, Ch. IV. [6] *Ibid.*, Book I, Ch. IV.

law, due to his peculiar metaphysic, that makes him minimize this phase of Vico's thought.

Croce draws a very sharp line between the history of philosophy and the history of human culture. Philosophic ideas have no continuous existence like brute things, but come into life whenever they are re-thought in their fullness by a kindred spirit (which may be very seldom). Hence the history of philosophy is unnecessary in the exposition of a single philosopher. But "in spite of the antipathy which we [Croce] ourselves admittedly feel," the attempt is made to trace in the last chapter and in the second appendix, the resemblance and analogies between Vico and later thought. According to the accepted canons of historical research it would seem that in order to establish the historical importance of a philosopher it is necessary to show, (1) that subsequent philosophers were acquainted with his works, and (2) that such acquaintance was a decisive influence in their thought. From this point of view it would seem that Vico was rather an interesting eddy in European thought, without influence on the main current. For in spite of the great attention devoted to him by Italians and by a few European historians like Michelet, Croce's own evidence shows that Vico's writings remained almost unknown in the eighteenth century, and none of the great philosophers of the nineteenth century seem to have been influenced by them. Nevertheless, Croce will not allow us to say that the work of Vico was historically insignificant. "Such language is blasphemy against history which allows nothing to be useless, and is always and throughout, the work of Providence" (p. 268). To support this, we are treated to a long list of rather superficial or far-fetched resemblances between Vico's thought and that of many of the subsequent great philosophical systems. Typical of these is the analogy between Vico and "the *a priori* synthesis of Kant which reconciles the real and the ideal, experience and the categories" (p. 238), as well as the attempt to assimilate

Vico's views on the struggle between the Roman patricians and plebeians, to the Marxian conception of the class-struggle based on the economic interpretation of history. Curiously enough Croce fails to note the resemblance between Vico and those who were closest to him outside of Italy, viz., the representatives of the German historical school of jurisprudence. But though Savigny, Puchta, *et al.* share his view of the "organic" nature of law, they do not seem to have been either directly or indirectly influenced by him.

The same lack of regard for ordinary historical perspective characterizes the special appendix added to the English translation, on the sources of Vico's theory of knowledge. Thus Croce fails to consider the influence of St. Augustine on Vico. This is remarkable not only because of the external resemblances between Vico's "eternal republic" and the City of God, but because Vico's teacher Ricci was an Augustinian, and Vico's autobiography and juristic works are full of acknowledgments of his debt to the great Bishop.[7]

All attempts to picture Vico as a forerunner of the nineteenth century are apt to miss the real significance of Vico for our own day. It is true that he was far ahead of eighteenth century mechanical theories of culture, but only because he was behind seventeenth century physics (see his puerile speculations on magnetism in his autobiography).[8] Vico was really a belated humanist of the type of Pico della Mirandola. But in his opposition to the spirit of the *Aufklärung* he caught vague glimpses of how this very rationalism or scientific spirit might be used to transform and elevate humanistic studies. This transformation Vico could not, because of his unsystematic and unscientific training, himself bring about. But his writing, like that of all genuinely contemplative minds that brood on conceptions, are full of suggestions that startle us by their modernity, e.g., his remarks on the fixed and the flux in lawmaking. The crudities and absurdities which

[7] *Opera Latina* (Ferrari), II, pp. 11, 19, 22, etc.
[8] *Oeuvres choisies*, I, pp. 54-55.

fill his pages are significant of the lack of discipline which typified the humanism of the Renaissance. The great service which the scientific movement that Vico opposed is rendering to real humanism is this very spirit of discipline, of rigorous self-control in the presence of intellectual temptation, which science is slowly bringing into our study of human life.

BOOK THREE

SCIENTIFIC ESSAYS

EINSTEIN'S THEORY OF
RELATIVITY

I. TIME AND SPACE

WITH THEIR COLUMNS crowded with news of grave economic and political disturbances at home and abroad, it was a rather liberal conception of what is really important that prompted our daily newspapers to find room for a report of a discussion on the nature of light and gravitation, held at a meeting of a London scientific society. The character of the report, however, but served to emphasize the tragic chasm between science and our popular intelligence of it. Apart from some ludicrous misapprehensions, our popular accounts suffered from confusing three distinct issues: (1) Einstein's original theory of relativity, (2) his later, more general theory, and (3) his theory of gravitation. The establishment of non-Newtonian mechanics and of non-Euclidean geometry are, again, different issues, the latter having been known to mathematicians for about a century.

Of Einstein's work the most revolutionary, and today the most firmly established, is the theory of relativity as formulated in 1905. Seven years later at the Brussels conference of the world's leading physicists, it was already referred to as "the older mechanics" in contrast with the more recent quanta theory especially associated with the name of Planck. Like other great innovations, the theory of relativity is based on a simple and even familiar principle, but one that had not been adequately developed before Einstein. Since Galileo and Newton it has been known that no mechanical experiment on a body can tell us whether it is at rest or moving uniformly in a straight line. Whatever metaphysics may say about absolute time and space, the physicist is restricted to measurable magnitudes, and he can tell whether a body is at rest or in uniform motion only by measuring its distance from some other physical body.

If we are in a Pullman car we tell whether our neighbor is walking or at rest, by referring to fixed elements in the car, e.g., the floor and the walls, independent of the fact whether our car is at rest or in uniform motion. We determine the motion of the car only in relation to the earth, the uniform motion of the earth only by reference to the sun, and the motion of the sun only by the variation of its distance from some "fixed" star. But whether our whole stellar or material universe is at rest or moving as a whole in a given direction, is a meaningless question to the experimental physicist. For he cannot discriminate between such rest and motion so long as he accepts the first principle of modern mechanics, viz., that a body not acted upon by external force maintains its state of rest *or* uniform motion, and that there is no mechanical means of telling which of these two alternatives is actually the fact.

All this is perfectly orthodox and has long been more or less familiar. Einstein's radicalism consisted in extending this principle of mechanics to the whole of physics, i.e., extending it to the realm of optics and electricity. In the latter fields, the principle of relativity had been disregarded because the triumph of the electric theory of light established the conception of a single ether filling the whole of space, so that the question whether a body moves with reference to this ether was practically equivalent to the question whether it moves with reference to absolute space. All experiments, however, invariably failed to show any evidence of the motion of the earth relative to the ether. The most famous and accurate of these experiments, the one originally devised by Professor Michelson in 1881, showed that the earth's motion does not affect the velocity of light, that the latter is the same in all directions precisely as if the earth were at rest rather than moving in a given direction. Many complicated and perversely ingenious explanations were invented to explain the discrepancy between these experiments and the established theory of a fixed ether. The most important and successful of these attempted explanations was the one devised by Lorentz, who suggested that all bodies are shortened in the direction of their motion, depending on the rate of their velocities to that of light. That mere motion should modify the length of a body may be no more surprising than that temperature should do so. But if all bodies are equally shortened, our measures of length, our foot-rules or yard-sticks, are also shortened, and our clocks or other time-measuring mechanisms are necessarily affected. This modification of our units of distance and time is the mathematical essence of the relativity theory, and the equations which describe it bear the name of Lorentz. Lorentz's procedure, however, seemed somewhat arbitrary and he did not ade-quately explain why all substances, including such diverse ones as sandstone and pine wood, should all contract in pre-cisely the same proportion.

It was at this point that there appeared in 1905 the epoch-making paper by Einstein, then a young employee in the Bern patent office, but already the author of some remarkable con-tributions to theoretic physics. With the courageous direct-ness of youth and genius, unburdened by too much academic knowledge of what others had done, Einstein went back to simple first principles. Disregarding completely all the arti-ficial and cumbrous theories of the ether, solid, fluid, elastic, labile, irrotational, gyrostatic, adynamic, etc., he got rid of all the artificial and perplexing difficulties in the explanation of optical and electrical phenomena in moving bodies, by boldly accepting the actual results of physical experimenta-tion. The actual results generalized give us the principle of relativity, viz., that *all* the laws of physical change are the same whether we suppose our system to be at rest or in uniform motion. Thus to revert to our previous illustration, a scientist experimenting in a moving Pullman car will find that the laws of electrical as well as mechanical phenomena are precisely the same as those found by a scientist experimenting in a building fixed to the earth. More particularly the velocity of light will be the same whether our car is at rest or in motion, and similarly if we substitute the whole terrestrial globe for the car. If we accept this principle, then, the negative results of all the attempts to measure the motion of the earth relative to the ether are not anomalies to be explained, but just what we ought to expect.

The reader may at this point suspect that I am unduly simplifying a principle which has widely been hailed as the most radical and paradoxical since the days of Copernicus. But I am really faithfully stating Einstein's principle, though substituting common words for the more elegant, accurate, and comprehensive language of mathematics. The paradoxical character of Einstein's work consists not in the principle of relativity, but in the fact that Einstein works out its consequences logically and in universal terms, whereas our common notions of time and space are based on and bound up with our ordinary experience in which the time it takes the light of different objects to reach us is such an infinitesimal part of a second that it can and must be disregarded for ordinary purposes. But when we come to deal with astronomic facts, the inaccuracy of our common ideas must be corrected.

To say that the identically same event must appear in one place and time to one observer and in another place and time to another observer may be surprising. But logic and rigorous experimentation are here on the side of the surprising. Thus if our Pullman scientist sends out an instantaneous light signal, let us say from the rear end of his moving train, the center of the resulting light disturbance will appear in all his experiments as fixed with reference to his car, whereas to the scientific observer outside of the train the center of the light disturbance will remain in a point of space from which the train is moving away. This dependence of the place of an event upon the observer's physical system shocks us because our imagination functions only between certain limits and breaks down when we try to image the addition or subtraction of the velocity of even a fast train to that of light, an addition which can be accurately stated to be less than 1/10,000,000 but which our imagination cannot really appreciate. Professor Michelson's experiments, however, clearly indicate that if the velocity of our train were a thousand times as great (i.e., equal to that of the earth in its orbit) the discrepancy mentioned above could clearly be detected with optical instruments of precision.

The most startling paradox, however, of the relativity theory is Einstein's discovery that two events which are simultaneous in one system, say our Pullman car, are not so in another system, e.g., when observed from the earth relative to which the car is moving. This does violence to our preconceived notion of an imaginary time flow that serves as the one absolute and unique time of all events in all possible universes. But the history of science shows that our subjective intuitions are far from infallible. At any rate, just as the question as to whether matter is or is not infinitely divisible is not to be settled by the nature of our subjective intuitions but by physical operations, so likewise must the actual physical time position be determined not by subjective notions but by some system of objective measurement, by clocks, chronometers, and the like. Here Einstein's epoch-making work was marvelously lucid. How do we establish in physics the simultaneous character of two events which take place in different portions of space? Clearly it must depend on some system of signaling. If you are in an astronomic observatory in possession of a standard clock and I want my clock to indicate the same time as yours, I telephone to you and when you say "twelve o'clock," I set mine at the same hour; but to be accurate, I must know the time it takes the telephone sound to reach me. Various experiments are possible by which we can determine this time. All such experiments, however, actually involve motion of the observer and dependence on optical or visible signals. As light is the most universal of all forms of signaling and as recent experiments on radium and cathode rays make it extremely unlikely that there can be any physical velocity greater than that of light, Einstein uses the method of light signaling to define the way in which all clocks can be synchronized or made to denote the same time. If you have a mirror which will instantly reflect back any light ray which I send you, I will know that so long as the velocity of light and the distance between us remain constant, the time at which you receive my signal is just half way between the time I send and the time I receive it.

Let us now suppose that you and I have thus synchronized our clocks, standing at the ends of a very long moving platform. If now we similarly get in touch with an observer relative to whom our platform is moving, we shall find that two events which are recorded as simultaneous by our two clocks are not recorded as simultaneous by his clock, for, while you and I must regard the time it takes light to travel from you to me as equal to the time it takes the light to make the return journey, the observer relative to whom we are both moving necessarily regards the two periods as unequal, since, as we are moving away from him, he must reckon that the signal he sends after us travels between us not only the length of our platform but also the distance that the platform itself moves during this period, whereas any ray returning to him travels the distance between us diminished by that which the platform itself moves during this period. Similarly, if two observers in the system relative to which we are moving have synchronized their clocks, they will record two events as simultaneous which to you or me are not simultaneous at all, since to you or me these two observers are precisely in the same relative position as if *they* were on a platform moving away from us.

The reader, who has clearly grasped the foregoing analysis of physical simultaneity, will see nothing paradoxical in the fact that distances between fixed points grow shorter and clocks are seen to grow slower as they move away from us.

For how do we determine the length of an object? When we are close up to it and it is at rest we lay off the length of a yardstick on it and count the number of times we do so. But when we deal with a distant or moving object we determine its length by the time it takes a light ray to pass over it. Now as it takes a longer time for a light ray to pass over an object that is moving in the same direction with it and a shorter time to pass over an object that is moving in the opposite direction, it follows that objects moving toward us with the light will be lengthened and objects moving away from us will be shortened.

That the rate at which a clock marks time will be changed by an increasing distance between it and the observer ought to be even clearer. If when you are going away on a long and continuous journey you write home at regular intervals, you should not be surprised that with the best possible mail service your letters will reach home at longer intervals, since each letter will have a greater distance to travel than its predecessor. If you were armed with instruments to hear the home clock ticking, you would find that if the rate of your traveling away from home keeps on increasing, the intervals between the successive ticks (i.e., its seconds) grow longer, so that if you traveled with the velocity of sound the home clock would seem to slow down to a standstill—you would never hear the next tick. Precisely the same is true if you substitute light rays for sound waves. If with the naked eye or with a telescope you watch a clock moving away from you, you will find that its minute hand takes a longer time to cover its five-minute intervals than does the chronometer in your hand, for it takes a longer time for the light from the later positions to reach you, and if the clock traveled with the velocity of light you would forever see the minute hand at precisely the same point. That which is true of the clock is, of course, also true of all time intervals which it measures, so that if you moved away from the earth with the velocity of light everything on it would appear as still as on a painted canvas. On the return journey, however, everything would seem correspondingly speeded up, so that when you reached home you would find the sum of your time account exactly the same as that of the home clock.

The last point may make vivid the fact that we have been dealing with a theory as to the possibility of different accounts of the same course of nature, and that these accounts must balance in the end if they are correct. This aspect of the theory has not been sufficiently emphasized by those scientific radicals who have no regard for the susceptibilities of their more timid and conservative brethren. But despite some hasty words—of which Einstein himself has not been altogether free—the corrections or refinements of the theory of relativity can no more be said to be subversive of established science or of our common sense ideas of time and space, than the pruning work of the gardener can be said to be destructive of his plants. What to the lay reader may at first seem a bewildering profusion of different times and places, time rates and velocities, may be readily and simply harmonized by the proper formulae or equations, just as we harmonize different accounts in yards and meters, or in dollars and pounds sterling.

The theory of relativity affords a remarkable instance of substantial progress in physics achieved by what might be viewed as a more accurate and comprehensive method of keeping our account of nature. The triumph of the electronic and other theories as to the "ultimate" constitution or structure of matter has tended to put in the shade the view of men like Mach, who insisted that the physicist can also gain by more critically examining his fundamental ideas, instruments and methods. Einstein's work, which professes to be inspired by Mach, shows that the latter's method may help us not only to introduce order into our science of electricity and to explain otherwise baffling optical and astronomical facts, but also to predict hitherto unsuspected facts such as the bending of light rays by gravity. But these developments and their more general significance deserve separate treatment.

II. THE LAW OF GRAVITATION AND THE MORE GENERAL THEORY OF RELATIVITY

FOR OVER TWO CENTURIES Newton's law of gravitation has served as the model or stock example of a law of nature. All efforts at scientific truth, even in the undeveloped social sciences, have regarded the discovery of similar laws as the ideal of scientific attainment. Any attempt, therefore, such as Einstein's, to modify and improve upon Newton's law must be viewed as having more than a merely technical interest.

The belief in simple and eternal laws of nature back of the persistent irregularity and instability of sensible phenomena, grew out of the ancient Neo-Platonic tradition that to the mind that approaches divine insight the book of nature is written in simple geometric lines. All the great founders of modern science, Copernicus, Kepler, Galileo, Descartes, and Newton shared this faith. The splendid results which followed their search for simple laws gave their faith the unique position of being the only one to have almost completely escaped serious assaults from the modern critical spirit. For despite their professions of welcome to anyone who can challenge their first principles, philosophers and scientists are made of the same human clay as theologians and lawyers or men of affairs, and have the same organic aversion for the thought which disturbs established and comfortable certainties. But many a faith that has been unassailable by direct frontal attack has been forced to yield or to reorganize by pressure from other quarters; and the faith in simple eternal laws of nature has in fact been undermined on the experimental side by the progressive improvement of our instruments of measurement, and on the mathematical side by the discovery of non-Euclidean geometry. The former has led to the view that our seemingly absolute laws of nature are but the statistical averages of the behavior of large numbers of inherently variable elements; and reflection on non-Euclidean geometry has pressed forward the thought that many diverse accounts of our fragmentary experience of the physical world can all claim to be equally true.

Everyone who has ever worked in a laboratory or with instruments of precision knows that the simple laws of nature, so clearly formulated in elementary and popular treatises, are never verified with absolute accuracy. The results of actual measurements always differ. We attribute this universal discrepancy between our theoretic formulae and our actual measurements not to our theory but to the "error" of our instruments. But the fact is that the refinement or improvement of our instruments never eliminates this discrepancy. On the contrary it often compels us to abandon the simple law in favor of a more complicated one. Boyle's law of the simple inverse proportionality between the volume and the pressure of gases has now yielded to the more complicated equation of Van der Waals; and the fate of Coulomb's law in electricity has indicated that the similarly formulated law of gravitation might also show itself to be but a first approximation in need of correction as our knowledge becomes more accurate.

That the acceptance of the theory of relativity involves some modification of the Newtonian theory of gravitation, and indeed of the whole Newtonian mechanics, is obvious from at least two considerations. The Newtonian mechanics is based on the assumption of the constancy of mass (popularly known as "the indestructibility of matter"), but from the theory of relativity it necessarily follows that the mass of a body varies with its velocity, and is different in the direction of its motion than in any direction perpendicular to it. Again, according to Newton the force of gravity is transmitted instantaneously or practically so, whereas according to the relativity theory there can be no greater velocity than that of light. According to the Newtonian mechanics the gravity or weight of a body is proportional to its mass or inertia, and the latter is a constant and independent constituent of energy. Modern experiments have suggested that possibly what we call mass is itself of electro-magnetic origin; or, at any rate, that radiant energy like light and cathode rays offer inertia or resistance to change which may well be called mass, and that such mass varies with its velocity. Thus considerations of experimental physics as well as deductions from the theory of relativity led Einstein, soon after publishing his paper of 1905, to the belief that energy itself has inertia or mass, and, therefore, gravity, and later to the hypothesis that gravitation depends not only on mass and distance but on other factors as well. Maxwell had already shown that light must exert pressure. It was natural for Einstein to take the next step and show that light must also have gravity. But the universal assumption that light travels in straight lines, and the difficulty of finding experimental tests for his theory, offered seemingly insuperable difficulties. To overcome these difficulties Einstein resorted to non-Euclidean geometry, made use of new mathematical methods, and widened or generalized his original theory of relativity.

In the halls of fame the names of Lobachevski and Riemann, the discoverers of non-Euclidean geometry, may seldom be heard. Riemann died in the prime of youth, and the imaginative genius of Lobachevski was smothered by the bleak prison doors of the remote and unenlightened University of Kazan. Yet these two men initiated one of the greatest revolutions in the history of human thought—they undermined for all time the unquestioned sanctity of axioms or first principles. For over two thousand years Euclid's geometry had served as the model for all science, philosophy, and theology. It was universally taken for granted—and most people still assume—that in every field there are axioms or first principles that cannot be doubted because they are self-evident, i.e., simple, clear and conclusive on simple inspection. Lobachevski showed that one of Euclid's axioms, that relating to parallel lines, could well be questioned: and Riemann went further in questioning the assumption (for that is what every axiom really is), that through any two points only one straight line can be drawn.)

Now though Euclidean geometry is still, because of its relative simplicity, the most convenient for ordinary lengths and areas, there is no mathematical or physical reason against the attempt to describe the astronomic universe in terms of one of these other geometries. It depends upon our choice as to what shall be the physical test of a straight line. If the captain of a ship defines a straight line on the surface of the earth or sea as the shortest distance between two points, he has in fact chosen the Riemannian geometry, since between two poles of the terrestrial sphere any number of such straight lines can be drawn. Similarly Einstein may with very good reason take the path of a light ray as the test of straightness. If in addition to this he also holds that light, like a projectile, proceeds not only under its own energy, but is deflected by a gravitational field, such deflection does not contradict the original definition of straightness, but only compels the use of non-Euclidean geometry.

Such a procedure may appear arbitrary to those who dislike all departure from the usual ways of doing things; and doubtless it is so. Only it must not be forgotten that the usual procedure is also arbitrary. Indeed, so long as man's knowledge of the universe is fragmentary, every attempt to formulate its nature must contain arbitrary elements. Arbitrary procedures, however, are justified if they lead to significant discoveries and in this respect Einstein's method is certainly justified.

In developing his theory of gravitation Einstein came into conflict with his own original theory of relativity, which he might also have called the theory of the absolute constancy of the velocity of light. Now if a gravitational field affects the path of light it cannot, according to Einstein's mathematics, leave its velocity unaffected. In his original theory he had shown that our ordinary units of time and distance were variable in relation to the constant velocity of light. What now is the constant with reference to which the velocity of light varies? The answer to this is that while theoretically the velocity of light can be constant only in the absence of marked gravitational influence, the mass of the earth is practically negligible in cosmic relations in which the sun and the "fixed" stars enter. Hence the original theory of relativity may be regarded as approximately true on the surface of the earth or wherever gravity may be viewed as a non-disturbing factor with reference to light.

To speak of the deflection of light by a gravitational field may seem to involve the old view of gravity as a force which pulls things together. This is not Einstein's view. His theory aims to be purely descriptive, and gravity appears in it not as a force, but rather as a property of a space or field. All we know of gravitation is that in certain portions of space all bodies, no matter what their constitution, are uniformly accelerated. Indeed, the phenomenon of deflected light would result in precisely the same way if there were no such thing as gravitation, but if the observer were moving with accelerated velocity in a direction perpendicular to the path of a light ray. The reader can make this clear to himself by imagining himself in an elevator going down with a uniform acceleration equal to that of a freely falling body. In such an elevator no free object can fall to the floor and a horizontally shot projectile, which, as seen from the earth, falls in a curved line, would here describe a perfectly horizontal line. Conversely if the path of the projectile or a light ray be perfectly horizontal to an observer on the earth, it will be curved to an observer in the elevator.

Considerations such as these have led Einstein to generalize his original theory of relativity. Instead of saying that the laws of nature are the same whether we suppose the observer to be at rest or in uniform motion, he now says the laws of nature are the same whether we suppose the observer to be at rest or in any kind of motion, accelerated or rotatory.

To realize something of the meaning of this statement, let the reader imagine a group of unusually gifted scientific observers confined since birth by some mysterious fate in a well-supplied Pullman car, and unable to learn anything of the outside world except by means of the light rays which stream in through their windows. (If this sounds too fanciful, let the reader remember that our earth is just such a car.) If such scientific observers begin to formulate the laws of nature they will naturally suppose their car to be at rest and all other things in motion in diverse ways. Their laws or equations of motions would be inordinately more complex than those familiar to us, if the car did not always move with uniform velocity. Imagine one of our scientists, as gifted as Copernicus or the early Pythagoreans, saying to himself, "Why not suppose that the earth outside of my windows is at rest and that my car is in motion?" If he did so, he would be able to simplify his account of nature enormously. The sudden lurch forward or backward of loose objects, for instance, would be explained not in some, to us, mysterious and complicated way, but by the inertia of things in motion. If now our scientist exultingly claimed before his fellow passengers that this proved that their car was really in motion, he might be stopped by one of them having the genius of Einstein and admonished as follows: "Hold on! You have undoubtedly discovered a new and simpler system of laws or equations to describe the course of nature. But what right have you to claim that your account is truer than the one which we have always hitherto used? Do you suppose that nature has no other care but to conduct herself in such a way as to make it possible for us to describe her conduct in simple laws? Besides I can show you a system of equations by which you can pass from every proposition in your old account of nature to a corresponding proposition in your new account."

The reader who knows something of the history of science will recognize that our example shows Einstein's later theory of relativity as reopening the issue between Galileo and those who condemned him for saying that the earth *is* in motion. If there is no unique absolute space and all motion is relative, it is just as true to say that the earth moves with reference to the car as to say that the car moves with reference to the earth. With our fixed habits of conception and expression, it may be extremely inconvenient or ridiculous to say that every time we drop an object the earth moves up to it; but it would be difficult to prove the falsity of this way of putting it. Similarly with regard to the revolution of the earth around its axis, which Einstein after the example of Mach, calls a revolution with reference to the "fixed" stars. It would be vain to repeat against Einstein the old arguments for the absolute rotation of the earth, based on Foucault's pendulum or the bulging of the earth at the equator. He shows that it is possible to define a space with regard to which the fixed stars are rotating. In such a space the earth may be considered at rest, and the phenomena which in Newtonian mechanics are called gravitational and centrifugal would change places. Since both are proportional to the mass of the earth there would be no experimental difference. Notice that Einstein does not justify the opponents of Copernicus or Galileo, or deny the tremendous progress which physics owes to the latter. Only he shows that to the extent that both parties in that famous controversy assumed a unique and absolute space they were equally wrong. In this respect, however, Einstein unconsciously brings fresh support to the views of the great Catholic physicist and historian of science, Pierre Duhem.

The greatest triumph of a physical theory is to predict hitherto unsuspected phenomena and to have these predictions experimentally confirmed. This triumph Einstein's theory of gravitation experienced when astronomers during a recent eclipse found that light rays passing near the surface of the sun are deflected just as Einstein predicted. This confirmation, however, by no means proves the whole theory of gravitation—much less his general theory of relativity. The general view that energy has gravity Einstein shares with Max Abraham and others who reject both theories of relativity; and the successful computations as to the course of light rays rest largely on certain independent subsidiary hypotheses. It is highly probable that some future scientist will improve on Einstein's complicated procedure in the theory of gravitation, precisely as Einstein's original paper on relativity improved on the methods of Lorentz and Larmor in the theory of electricity.

It would be absurd to attempt to indicate in the tail end of an article the many philosophical bearings of the theory of relativity. Possibly, however, I may stimulate the reader's own reflection by peremptorily firing at him the following suggestions:

1. The theory of relativity has dealt a death blow—at least so far as scientific physics is concerned—to the view that space and time are empty forms or vessels existing independently of, and possibly prior to, their material contents. Time and space are for physics the correlated numbers or dimensions of material things and events; and in a quiet unexpected way our time and space measures have now been shown to be dependent on each other as well as on the material system of which they are aspects. But though every physical system can thus be said to have its own time and space, the theory of relativity by establishing formulae for correlating all possible physical systems, establishes a universal time and space in the new sense.

2. By showing physical time to be but one aspect of natural events, the theory of relativity reinforces the legitimacy of the great philosophic tradition of viewing things from their eternal aspect. Indeed, Minkowski, one of the most brilliant mathematical minds of modern times, has actually shown how on the basis of the relativity theory the whole of

our three dimensional physics can be viewed as a chapter in a four dimensional geometry—time being the fourth dimension. To the popular mind the notion of a four dimensional world has, because of the spiritistic use of it by Zöllner, been associated with irresponsible and unintelligible vagaries. But Minkowski's four dimensional geometry is a sober, useful and vivid picture of our changing world. Portions of H. G. Wells's Time-Machine can give it popular representation. Indeed, whenever we think of any physical event, have we not before us something spread over a time interval as over space?

3. There is a popular philosophic tradition according to which all things are so interconnected that everything makes a difference to everything else. This view is generally fortified by a quotation from Tennyson to the effect that a complete botany of the flower in the crannied wall must include a complete anthropology and theology. Against this view, the original theory of relativity shows that certain motions, while they affect our units of measurement, nevertheless do not affect the final results or laws of nature which we thus obtain, just as figuring the value of your dollars in terms of francs does not change the actual amount in your pocket. You may glorify the unity of the world or the interconnectedness of things as much as you please, but you cannot, without denying the validity of physical science, deny that certain things or aspects of the world are independent of others.

4. It is difficult to determine the precise physical significance which Einstein attaches to his later and more general theory of relativity. You bang your fist on the table, and Einstein shows you how to find a mathematical system of co-ordinates, or time and space elements, in which your fist is defined to have been at rest and the co-ordinates or distances of other objects to have been changing accordingly. This is undoubtedly a great mathematical achievement to the lasting credit of Einstein and his co-worker Grossman, but what bearing, you ask, has it on the physical nature of the world in which

we live? Einstein's answer seems to be that the fact of your bringing down your fist is indifferent to the various mathematical descriptions of it, just as it is indifferent as to whether you express it in English or Gaelic. On the other hand Einstein believes that there are laws of nature and that these laws are expressed by mathematical equations whose essential form is unchanged by any change of co-ordinates or space-time elements which enter into them. If he is justified in asking "What has nature to do with our co-ordinate systems?" why not ask, "What has nature to do with the invariance of our equations?" Might it not be possible to give a physical meaning to the changes of co-ordinates as well as to the invariance of the equations? In any case it seems a fact that certain mathematical formulae or descriptions serve more effectively than others as keys to all sorts of natural phenomena. If people had kept on saying that the earth is still and the sun in motion would they have made the discoveries which followed the other way of putting it?

Whatever may be the fate of the theory of relativity it has undoubtedly opened up new regions of thought by suggesting new possible connections between fundamental ideas like energy, space, matter, and gravity, and can there be any greater service to the human mind than this opening up of new fields?

ROADS TO EINSTEIN

THE PUBLICATION of all these books [1] on the theory of relativity, besides the numerous newspaper and magazine articles addressed to the general public, is an impressive testimony of the extent to which cosmic problems still solicit the human mind. Doubtless a great deal of the popular interest in the theory of relativity is temporary and somewhat meretricious. The irresponsible assertion that there are twelve men who understand the fantastic newspaper accounts of it has doubtless served to add to the fascination which the unintelligible always exercises on men's minds, much as forbidden fruit stimulates desire. But behind this there is certainly a great deal of genuine rational curiosity. Despite the insistence of intellectual mediocrity that the proper study of mankind is man, nothing is of such truly human interest as the nature of the physical world in which we live. Moreover, to gain a genuinely new fundamental idea such as is involved in the theory of relativity is an experience akin to that which comes in the highest creative art or religion—a liberation from the dead complacency of the accepted views and an enlargement of our being by an enlarged vision of new possibilities.

Can this new insight into the structure of our physical world be brought home to the general public? The answer depends not only on the expositor but also on the previous training and present intellectual zeal of the reader. A thorough technical mastery of Einstein's theory of gravitation requires a knowledge of new branches of higher mathematics;

[1] Albert Einstein, *Relativity, The Special and General Theory, a Popular Exposition;* A. S. Eddington, *Space, Time and Gravitation;* H. A. Lorentz, *The Einstein Theory of Relativity;* M. Schlick, *Space and Time in Contemporary Physics;* E. Freundlich, *The Foundations of Einstein's Theory of Gravitation;* S. Alexander, *Space, Time and Deity;* A. N. Whitehead, *An Enquiry Concerning the Principles of Natural Knowledge;* A. N. Whitehead, *The Concept of Nature.*

but the fundamental principles are all simple enough, and Einstein himself states them in his book with masterly clarity. It is folly, however, to expect that his modification of the older theories should be clear to those—a greater multitude than is generally admitted—who have no true idea as to what are the fundamental principles of the older Galileo-Newtonian mechanics. There is no royal road in science, not even for King Demos. Even with the best guides, the hill of vision is steep and rocky. It also takes time before the eye can become adjusted to the new and more sweeping views. But if the king is tired or impatient and wants to be entertained, let him call the court jesters, the movies and the short-story magazines.

Professor Eddington's book is addressed to readers who, though without technical knowledge of the subject, are willing to learn and are not scared by a few mathematical symbols. Professor Eddington is the foremost English expounder of Einstein, and it was his report that first introduced Einstein's theory of gravitation to the British public at a time when America was cut off from German publications by the blockade. But though it is based on a thorough mastery of the mathematics of the subject, and written with a great deal of verve, the book suffers from a certain systematic unclearness as to fundamentals. There is no very clear distinction between mathematical analogies and physical identities. This is well illustrated in the use of the term "curvature of space." Thus, also, the shortening of distances and the slowing up of clocks in moving systems are spoken of sometimes as physical facts (in the manner of Lorentz and Fitzgerald) and sometimes as mathematical consequences of our conventions as to measurement (which is Einstein's contribution to the subject). Obviously these two different conceptions cannot be true at the same time. Professor Eddington also confuses physical relativity, the relativity of physical measurements to each other, with the entirely different issue of the relativity of physical occurrences to a human mind.

The newspaper article of Lorentz—it is only in its English translation that the publishers have padded it out with miscellaneous additions into a book—is by a master who may rightly be called the author of the electromagnetic theory of relativity. It does one good to note the characteristic generosity of great men of science in the enthusiasm of the older master for the younger man who has improved on his work by a method requiring the fascinating boldness of youth. Unfortunately the standard of foreign newspaper articles on scientific subjects is above that of America and one cannot recommend Lorentz's article to those entirely unacquainted with theoretic physics.

Einstein's own book is a really remarkable achievement in clear exposition. The great masters are generally their own best expounders. For the same quality of mind which makes for great scientific achievement, viz., a faith in simple principles strong enough to master the labyrinth of factual details, is precisely the quality which makes for clarity of exposition. At any rate Einstein's exposition certainly has the supreme merit of always keeping the fundamental principles in the foreground and never losing sight of the woods for the trees. If any reader after a fair effort cannot grasp the fundamental ideas of this book, he has only his own defective education to blame. This, however, does not mean that the book offers no difficulties to one who wishes to master the new theory of relativity. But the main difficulties will be found to be due not to any obscurity in the new ideas but rather to the inertia of the older ideas which persist even after we have learned that they are not logically necessary. For our ideas are mental habits and it requires training or habituation as well as understanding to change them. The reader who understands that numbers may be written in a system where the unit is 12 rather than 10, will be surprised at the number of natural errors he will fall into when he begins to calculate in a duodecimal system. We have the recorded remarks of an English statesman who could see only the most paradoxical results if British coinage were changed to a decimal system. So likewise all the paradoxes which have been so prominent in the popular discussion of the theory of relativity result from unguardedly importing the naïve assumptions of the older ideas into the discussion of newer ideas which are inconsistent with them.

The reason for abandoning the old idea of time and space units that are absolute for all possible physical systems is clearly brought out in Schlick's book. Schlick, and even more clearly Freundlich, will also help the reader to realize the newer conception of geometry, not as an *a priori* science but as a branch of empirical physics. Freundlich's book is also especially clear in its explanation of the newer idea of gravitation. But it is doubtful if even these books can make the conception of the finitude of space perfectly clear to those entirely unfamiliar with the older literature of non-Euclidean geometry.

But the principal obstacle which, I think, troubles lay readers most and which these books do not remove is the difficulty of working oneself into the purely descriptive point of view which is habitual with trained physicists who, like Einstein, have come under the influence of Ernst Mach. The ordinary man knows that when he moves he exerts himself and that his engine or car will not move unless he does something to it. Hence, when he hears the physicist say that rest and motion are relative, and that the motion of a car relative to the earth is the same as the motion of the earth relative to the car, he is completely mystified. Surely we do not set the earth in motion every time that we take a walk or even nod. This difficulty can be removed only by a full realization of the standpoint which physicists call kinematics, which is the point of view of an observer who stands outside of the stream of events and knows nothing of their causes but describes all happenings as accurately as his instrument of measurement will allow. To such an observer motion is not a property of a body but merely a change of distance between one body and others. Such a change of distance is obviously the same whether we say that A moves from B or B moves from A.

When the reader has realized that for the physicist motion is merely the change of distance between objects, he is on the road to understand why Einstein and others feel so strongly that no one body is privileged by nature to be the unique starting point for the measurement of all motion. Common sense and even natural history are interested in particular things and can make them centers of description. But theoretic physics is interested in formulating invariable laws of nature and these laws cannot depend on the arbitrary choice of Paris or Berlin as our centers of measurement. Indeed, it may help to eliminate too easily reliance on the word "relativity," if we refer to Einstein's theory as one that affirms the absoluteness of the laws of nature for all possible systems of measurement.

In this connection it is important to emphasize that Einstein's procedure involves no hypotheses or theory as to the hidden structure of matter or as to the forces or other agencies behind the veil of phenomena. This procedure, known in the history of physics as the abstractive method, is, of course, not Einstein's invention. It has been followed by the greatest physicists from the days of Galileo and Newton to those of Fourier and Willard Gibbs. But in recent times it has been somewhat eclipsed by the triumph of the electron theory which led many to believe that we could through hypotheses as to the structure of the atom reach the ultimate nature of matter. It is the great achievement of Einstein to show that not only may the science of physics be unified but new phenomena may be predicted on the basis of the old abstractive method. The successful prediction of the bending of light rays has been most impressive to the experimental physicists, but to those interested in the general view of the cosmos the unifying effect of the relativity theory on the whole science of physics is of even greater significance. Since the beginning of their science, physicists had been trying in vain to explain the phenomena of electricity and optics on the basis of mechanics, i.e., on the principles of matter and motion. So unsuccessful did these persistent efforts prove, that at the end of the nineteenth century the effort was reversed and attempts made to derive the laws of mechanics from those of electro-magnetism, which had proved so successful in the field of optics. But the phenomena of gravitation proved indigestible to all electro-magnetic theories. It is Einstein's undoubted achievement to have eliminated unbridgeable chasms between the different parts of physics by successfully uniting the laws of gravitation with the laws of motion and showing that Newton's laws of motion and Maxwell's laws of electricity are subject to the same kinematic principles. In this Einstein has had the good sense to guard against any premature synthesis such as has been attempted by some of his more radical followers like Weyl.

Why, in spite of the inevitable and for many quite insurmountable difficulties, should one who is not a technical physicist bother with the theory of relativity? A great many laymen have doubtless been bullied into undertaking a study of it by the assertion that it marks a revolution in the history of mankind as great as that of Copernicus. But all assertions as to the extent of the revolution which the theory of relativity is bound to create have been of the nature of daring prophecy rather than cautious summary of evidence; and prophecy in the intellectual realm is even more hazardous than in the material realm. Certainly the theory of relativity will not immediately affect the price of oil or even bring relief to the sorely harried victims of the war in Europe. But the old and irrepressible questions as to the bourne of time and space which have agitated the human mind at least since the days of Aristotle, Plotinus, and St. Augustine have received fresh light. Even if the theory of relativity is definitely refuted by physical tests, which is certainly not impossible, its value as a philosophic stimulant will not have been wiped out.

Dr. Whitehead is one of the few living men qualified by the requisite knowledge of mathematics, physics, and philosophy to deal adequately with the wider aspects of the theory of relativity. But his two books, though of the highest importance, are certainly not popular reading. In his stupendous attempt to reconstruct the whole framework of the scientific view of nature, he has elaborated a new terminology of his own, and one must read his book several times to be sure of penetrating to his intellectual motives. Still Dr. Whitehead's main contention is in itself clear and illuminating. He tries to begin with the flow of natural events and to invent a system of concepts to fit it. According to his view, the new physics overthrows the old mechanical philosophy so far as the latter believed in material points and instants of time as determining the character of events. The logically unsatisfactory character of the older mechanical views has long been generally recognized. Physicists have known that "points" and "instants" are not facts but logical limits. But in the absence of a workable alternative method the old mechanical view was useful and even indispensable. The theory of relativity suggests new views which make reality consist of a flow of events rather than of hypothetical instants. It would be difficult to overestimate the importance of this fact for the social sciences which have always drawn their models of scientific method from the physical sciences. The mechanical method in the social sciences has hitherto led to the systematic ignoring of the category of possibility and hence to a tragically systematic impoverishment of the conception of human nature. But it will require a great deal more development of Dr. Whitehead's compact theses before these points can be made clear to students of social science.

Liberal western civilization, beginning with Greek rationalism, is opposed to the oriental caste distinction between the esoteric and the exoteric. Free civilization means that everyone's reason is competent to explore the facts of nature for himself. But the recent development of science, involving ever greater mastery of complicated technique, means in effect a return to an artificial barrier between the uninitiated layman and the initiated expert. If, therefore, the essence of western civilization is to be preserved, we need not only a higher level of general education but a class of genuine popularizers who will aim not to humor tired minds but to guide man's thirst for knowledge to the sources of its deepest satisfaction.

The following commentary by Cecil Barnes on this discussion and reply by the Author appeared in the New Republic, *September 28, 1921.*

QUESTIONS IN EINSTEIN

SIR: In your issue of July 6, 1921, Mr. Morris R. Cohen reviewed several books on the Einstein Theory of Relativity. Some of these books discuss the "slowing down" of a "moving clock," but leave one rather puzzled as to just what this means. Perhaps Mr. Cohen would be willing to explain.

"As a consequence of its motion, the clock goes more slowly than when at rest." (*Theory of Relativity* by Albert Einstein, page 37 of English Edition.) Now to me this is an ambiguous statement. I can think of three things it might mean:

(1) That moving a clock has such an effect on its mechanism as to make it actually run slower. This slowing down would be similar to the effect on a pendulum clock caused by placing it in an elevator descending with increasing acceleration—a slowing down explicable by classical mechanics, and due to the lessened pull of gravity on the pendulum.

(2) That though the clock runs at the same speed ("same speed" as here used to be interpreted by common sense, and not by any new conception based on relativity) it *appears* to run slower as seen by a stationary observer, because the observer, at any moment, sees the hands where they were when

the light then causing his retinal image left the clock, and the light reaching him at each second has further to travel than the light which reached him the second before.

(3) That the clock actually runs slower (as in case 1), not, however, because rapid motion retards its mechanism, but because being a clock intended to keep the time at a moving point, it was designed and regulated to keep the time proper to such a point; that is, a slower time, so that it differs from an ordinary clock, as a clock keeping mean solar time differs from a clock keeping sidereal time. In cases 1 and 3 there would, of course, be a still further retardation apparent to a stationary observer for the reasons stated in case 2. That there are two such separable retardations is pointed out by Eddington (page 24, Cambridge Edition).

Which of the three agrees with the Theory of Relativity? Or is there yet another way in which a moving clock can be said to "slow down"?

CECIL BARNES.

SIR: Of Mr. Barnes's alternatives the last comes nearest to what Einstein means by saying that a clock in motion is slower than if it were at rest. Mr. Barnes, however, does not sufficiently emphasize the new principle of relativity.

Alternative 2 is true in the older, or Newtonian, relativity, and is not questioned in the newer theory.

Alternative 1, if we leave out the reference to gravity, represents the view of Lorentz and Fitzgerald that there is an actual physical slowing up of all clocks in motion—in motion with reference to the ether or absolute space.

According to Einstein, however, we can never physically determine "actual" or absolute rest and motion, and no one clock can, therefore, be said to represent "the" true or absolute time. But of any two similarly constructed clocks that are in motion relative to each other, we may take either one as at rest and then the other will be found to be relatively slower —and this apart from the effect of increasing distance noted

[241]

in alternative 2. Thus, if I take the earth as at rest and the sun as in motion, the time of an event, say the period of a light wave, would be longer on the sun than on the earth. This follows from Einstein's original or special theory of relativity, which takes no account of gravitation. The additional considerations which the latter involves are not necessary to answer Mr. Barnes's question.

MORRIS R. COHEN.

A PHILOSOPHY OF
MATHEMATICS

Professor Brunschvicg's substantial work,[1] which may be described as an attempt at a philosophy of mathematics on an historical basis, is divided into seven books. The first six of these books are in the main historical, giving something of the history of mathematical science as well as of mathematical philosophy. In the last book the author gives his own views in the form of a digest of the previous historical material. As the titles of the different books indicate, the author has endeavored to combine the topical with the chronologic treatment of the subject, and this he has skillfully accomplished by means of very generous omissions. Thus the book on arithmetic ends with Pythagoras, and the next book, on geometry, begins with Plato. The book on the evolution of arithmetism, coming after the criticism of Kant and Comte, deals rather lightly with the arithmetical ideas of Cauchy, Renouvier, and Méray. Thus the whole history of arithmetic from the days of Pythagoras to almost the middle of the nineteenth century is omitted, and with it all attempt to estimate the leading arithmetical ideas of men like Gauss or what is technically called the theory of numbers. Similarly M. Brunschvicg dispenses with any systematic treatment of the significance of modern work on the theory of surfaces, line geometry, theory of functions, or vector analysis. Nonmetrical geometry, which some have regarded as one of the most original creations of the nineteenth century, is hardly mentioned (Von Staudt's name does not occur at all). In view of the vast amount of ground covered in this volume, these omissions (like the omission of any reference to the influential though superficial views on mathematics of men like Mill and Schopenhauer), would not be noted except for

[1] Léon Brunschvicg, *Les Étapes de la Philosophie Mathématique* (Paris, 1912).

[243]

M. Brunschvicg's assertion (p. vii) that only in a complete survey of the progress of mathematical thought can truth be secured.

The three chapters which constitute Book I, are devoted respectively to the arithmetical operations of "primitive" peoples, the mathematical content of the Rhind Papyrus, and the Pythagorean philosophy. No logical coherence of these topics is claimed, nor is there any intention to regard the Pythagorean philosophy as on the same level or "stage" as "primitive" or Egyptian thought. The reason given for bringing these topics together is that it is necessary to study the mathematical processes of naïve intelligence as well as the body of reflective thought. (M. Brunschvicg uses instead of the latter, the term *dogmatic*.) There is no attempt, however, to show any vital or organic connection between the dogmatic thought of Pythagoras and the unreflective thought embodied in contemporary Greek mathematics. M. Brunschvicg does, undoubtedly, give us many ingenious suggestions as to how reflection on the problems of mathematics determined the philosophy of Plato, Descartes, and Kant, but he never asks the question, why reflective thought, or the dogmatic tradition, arises at all. If he had, he might not have so readily accepted the prevailing misology which regards all dogmatic or philosophic systems as bodies of death, shutting up spontaneous thought, and having no function except the "bookish" or pedagogic one.

Although Book II is entitled Geometry it by no means restricts itself to that topic, but contains very suggestive accounts of the mathematical philosophy of Plato, Aristotle, Euclid, and the Cartesian school. It seems rather peculiar that Pythagoras should be treated only under the head of arithmetic, and not at all under the head of geometry. But, according to M. Brunschvicg's theory (in which he follows Milhaud), the Pythagorean philosophy considered only finite integers as real, and the discovery of incommensurables led to its breakdown and to the rise of the Platonic philosophy. This view offers grave difficulties, especially in view of the contributions which the Pythagoreans undoubtedly made to geometry and the antiquity which Aristotle attributes to the discovery of incommensurables; but it offers a very effective approach to the philosophy of Plato which is thus presented as an effort to show that the intelligible extends beyond the realm of numbers. The Platonic method is shown to consist in the regressive analysis of the sensible data until we come to fundamental hypotheses, and these by a dialectic process are deduced from supersensible principles. The first part of this, the belief that the function of thought is one of analysis, that it is exercised with the aid of the science of numbers and figures, and that step by step it discovers the mathematical relations in the texture of phenomena (p. 70), M. Brunschvicg regards as the essence of positive science and the truth of philosophy, and in that sense Plato did succeed in extracting from mathematics a universal method; but the second part, connecting the mathematical numbers with Ideas or ideal numbers, led to obscurity which caused the downfall of the whole Platonic system, and its replacement by that of Aristotle until the Renaissance. Here, as elsewhere, the author confuses the stages of his discourse with the facts of real history. In point of fact, of course, Platonism did not suffer any such fall or total eclipse, and in the form of Neo-Platonism at least (which does not happen to interest M. Brunschvicg), it kept up a rather vigorous existence. Moreover, the Neo-Platonism of the Renaissance was not, as he supposes, altogether positivistic, but full of metaphysical speculation, as the writings of Kepler and Galileo amply testify.

Although Aristotle is painted as an empiricist, founding his organon on biologic science, and discarding the Platonic metaphysic (or metamathematics), still our author seems to have for him very little intellectual sympathy. If Platonism is "the science of the connection between ideas—real science," Aristotelianism is "apparent science, the science of verbal classification" (p. 45). M. Brunschvicg seems to be under the

[245]

impression that Aristotle got his categories from the grammars of his day, and his grasp of Aristotle's thought in this connection is shown by the fact that he does not discuss the latter's theory of predication or the importance of the category of οὐσία. Possibly if he had, he would not have made the astounding and indefensible identification of the modern logistic movement with the syllogistic of Aristotle, since the former involves a radical criticism of the substantive-attribute theory of predication. In this connection it is well to note that it is essential to Aristotelianism to restrict mathematics to quantity, which modern logistics certainly does not. M. Brunschvicg also admits that the view of modern logic which reduces the major premise to an hypothesis is a departure from the Aristotelian theory.

It is significant of our author's own thought that he does not sympathize with Aristotle's effort to get from the order of knowing to the order of being (p. 79).

The *Elements* of Euclid is regarded as the product of the same spirit as the *Analytics* of Aristotle. Both succeeded in acquiring the appearance of eternal truth independent of historical origins (p. 85). But while outwardly modeled on the Aristotelian logic of classes, the material for a logic of relations is found in the *Elements,* especially in the books on proportion and on irrationals. But the Greeks could not free themselves from the view that mathematics is necessarily a qualitative study of quantity. It required the technical extension of modern mathematics before the Cartesian generalization of geometry could become possible. By extending Algebra over the realm of geometry the Platonic idea of a universal mathesis is revived, and the algebraic equation becomes "the reason of the determination of the universe" (p. 121). Quantity is no longer drawn by abstraction from the observation of things, but is established *a priori* by the power of reason (p. 123). There is, to be sure, still in Descartes a certain amount of dualism between spatial quantity and pure algebraic quantity, but these are united into one by Malebranche and Spinoza. In the latter's *Ethics,* mathematics again becomes the science of pure ideas or reality (pp. 147-148).

Book III, dealing with the development of the infinitesimal calculus, and especially with the philosophy of Leibniz, seems to be merely an elaborate interlude or mere episode in this intellectual drama; for in Book IV, devoted to Kant and Comte, the Cartesian thought is resumed and space remains "with Kant the necessary mediator, with Comte the privileged mediator, for the connection of the abstract relations which constitute science, and the empirical facts which constitute reality" (p. 341). Thus the logic of spatial relations continues to dominate science. But the discovery of non-Euclidean geometry has shown that mathematics does not give us a unique determination of space, and the development of analysis has shown that the latter is not dependent on spatial intuition, while the development of physics has shown that the classical mechanics is not the only possible scientific view of the physical world. Hence, according to M. Brunschvicg, the reaction against the logic of spatial relations in the latter part of the nineteenth century. This reaction naturally takes the form of a Neo-Pythagoreanism, or revival of a philosophy or logic of numbers, and a Neo-Aristotelianism or revival of the logic of classes. Books V and VI are devoted to these two movements respectively.

Book V, on the Evolution of Arithmetism, is the shortest in the volume and seems to grow out of a preconceived scheme rather than out of its subject matter. It treats in the main of two topics: (1) the arithmetization of modern analysis, and (2) a certain French philosophic movement rightly called *finitisme* (Renouvier, etc.). The treatment of the former topic is very inadequate. M. Brunschvicg does not seem to realize that the movement began at the end of the eighteenth century with the work of Gauss, and even as far back as Lagrange, and that it is essentially part of the effort of modern mathematics to insist on absolute rigor in demonstration and to eliminate spatial intuition, because the latter—apart from non-

Euclidean geometry—is often misleading and almost always inadequate. The result of this purely technical movement has been to establish methods for our calculus or analysis that are demonstrably just as rigorous as the methods of finite arithmetic. Now the establishment of this homogeneity between the finite integers and other mathematical entities like irrationals, complex numbers, etc. (the latter being operations of integers), does certainly render the position of *finitisme* (Renouvier, Evellin, etc.) untenable, but it does not seem to be decisive of the question of nominalism with which M. Brunschvicg connects it. Those who believe that imaginaries, etc., are pure fictions or nominal symbols must now believe that 2 or 7 are likewise so, whereas those who hold integers to represent something objective in nature, must now hold complex and higher numbers to be equally objective. The whole question really depends on whether we shall call all operations or transformations "mental," and to the solution of this question mathematics supplies only part of the material.

It might be noted, to the discomfiture of M. Brunschvicg's historical schematism, that the position of Renouvier that only finite integers are representative of reality, is really a reassertion of the Aristotelian doctrine that all actuality is finite and the infinite never more than potential; while logistic philosophers like Mr. Russell are in fact *Platonic* realists. However, in the sixth book M. Brunschvicg's sins are more serious than schematic illusions.

This sixth book consists of three chapters, one giving an account of the formation of the logistic philosophy of mathematics, and the other two the author's criticism of the work of Mr. Russell.

The development of this philosophy is traced to the growth of symbolic logic and to the *Mengenlehre* of Cantor. The purely philosophical motives such as those which Russell owes to Moore are ignored—probably because M. Brunschvicg does not think it necessary to inform himself carefully about contemporary English philosophy (see his reference to Reid, p. 390), and seems to be unaware of the existence of a problem about the nature of judgment. But even the technical mathematical influences are not adequately appreciated. The account of the development of symbolic logic is based on insufficient secondary sources (see e.g., his reference to Peirce, p. 379), so that he does not realize how completely the logic of classes is subordinated in modern symbolic logic. While the account of the influence of Cantor's work is somewhat more satisfactory, M. Brunschvicg's schematism makes him miss here the predominant importance of the arithmetization of mathematics. The latter movement has furthered the main logistic thesis, viz., the identity of *pure* mathematics and symbolic logic, first by insisting on rigorous logical proof where formerly we were satisfied to rely on self-evidence or intuition, and secondly, by making the field of mathematics more homogeneous, it has pressed the necessity of greater generality in the definition of the fundamental operations of arithmetic. What, for instance, do we mean by *multiplication,* if this process applies to series? Here, contrary to M. Brunschvicg's assumption of the complete futility of symbolic logic for mathematical investigations (p. 426), symbolic logic becomes a real and needed help in mathematical research.

Although M. Brunschvicg puts his criticisms of the logistic philosophy in historical form, they are, in the vicious sense, *a priori,* i.e., they are based on assumed self-evident principles which the subject matter in no way necessitates. Among the principles which M. Brunschvicg assumes and from which he argues are: (1) that all logic is purely analytic, in the sense that it is based on the principle of identity, and hence there can be nothing in the conclusion which was not already in the premises; and (2) that truth can relate only to actually existent entities, hence a pure mathematics or symbolic logic which applies as well to physically nonexistent entities must be futile for real "science." Now if the claims of modern logistics are inconsistent with these principles, may we not

[249]

venture to ask whether perhaps these principles are false?

Let us consider the matter from the point of view of the enlightened empiricism which M. Brunschvicg professes and which insists on an examination of the facts of a case instead of an obstinate reliance on preconceived principles which tell us that certain facts cannot possibly be.

The fundamental thesis of the logistic movement is that the whole of what we call pure mathematics can be logically deduced from certain principles which are also the principle of symbolic logic. This deduction they claim not only as possible but as actually having been accomplished in diverse works of which Russell's *Principles of Mathematics,* and Whitehead and Russell's *Principia Mathematica* may be taken as examples. Obviously the only way to answer this claim is not to keep on shouting forever: "This is impossible because logic can never give us anything but tautologies"; but to show that this alleged deduction or derivation breaks down at definite points. This is precisely what M. Brunschvicg does not do. Indeed there is strong evidence of the fact that he has not read the *Principia* at all, or the *Principles* with any care. The evidence for this serious charge against one who writes as an historian and claims for his judgment the character of being in some sense definitive (p. 394), is to be found in his claim that the whole of Russell's system is founded on the Aristotelian logic of classes and on an ontologic realism as to the existence of these classes. As a matter of fact the logic and ontology of classes figures very slightly in the main argument of the *Principles* and not at all in the *Principia.* Explicitly and emphatically the authors of the *Principia* point out that the ontologic existence of classes is in no way necessary for the argument; and the theory of types constructed to do away with the difficulty in the notion of a class of all classes is already indicated in the appendix to the *Principles.*

The other objections brought against the logistic position are based on the same lack of familiarity with the content of the *Principia* or *Principles*. Thus one chapter is devoted to an attack on the idea of an absolute deduction. But the *Principia* explicitly disclaims the idea of an absolute deduction and merely claims that the principles it sets up are sufficient to enable us to deduce the laws of mathematics from them; and while in the *Principles* Russell does argue for the Newtonian conception of absolute time and space, and the real existence of points and instants, his arguments only prove that the Newtonian position does not involve any self-contradiction, and can, therefore, logically exist. A careful reading of the *Principles*, however, shows that this argument is not a necessary part of the main thesis, and Mr. Russell, if I understand him, has already modified his position in regard to the absolute existence of points. But even if he has not, it would seem fair to demand of a historian that he distinguish between the fundamental thesis of an important intellectual movement and the particular beliefs of its most noted philosophical representative.

Another set of difficulties assigned as the cause of the alleged dissolution of the logistic philosophy, is the difficulty arising from an analytic interpretation of mathematics. Assuming quite needlessly that all logical procedure must be analytical, M. Brunschvicg finds in Russell's and Couturat's assertion about mathematical judgments being synthetic, evidence of the bankruptcy of logistics which professes to carry out the Leibnizian idea of a universal calculus and to be opposed to the Kantian view of a synthesis founded in *a priori* intuition. The procedure of this argument is based on a violent refusal to understand what is really very clearly stated. Russell, in his *Principles* and especially in his book on Leibniz, and Couturat in his *Principes,* very clearly and explicitly point out that logic cannot be founded exclusively on the principle of identity. This, however, is in no way an argument for the Kantian position that the proposition $7 + 5 = 12$ is logically indemonstrable or based on sensory intuition. That logical procedure involves some form of *intellectual* intuition or

[2 5 1]

apprehension is, of course, necessary for the logistic position, and Russell and Couturat have clearly admitted it. In this connection M. Brunschvicg might be reminded that, according to his own account, the Aristotelian syllogism involves more than the principle of identity (whence the dogma, nothing in the conclusion which was not already in the premises), and that there is a tinge of biologic analogy in the Aristotelian conception of two premises uniting to generate a conclusion.

Still another argument against the logistic position appears incidentally (p. 402), but is very significant of the author's own position. According to the logistic position *pure* mathematics is concerned only with the question whether a proposition does or does not imply another proposition. Now as false propositions also have implications, M. Brunschvicg is led to the view that the truths of pure mathematics can be of no significance for an objective science. "Truth that one could find in the highest degree in the logical fancies of an Edgar Poe or in the development of a systematic delirium, is surely not the categoric and intrinsic truth which is the condition of scientific knowledge" (p. 402). This is a popular fallacy based on the false belief that truth and science can deal only with the actual. If this were true there could be no such a theory as pure arithmetic. $2 + 2 = 4$ would be true only if actual chairs or tables were referred to. It would have no meaning when applied to the operations of a frictionless engine. This view, however, would make a science of physics impossible. Consider the situation when we have two rival physical hypotheses. Of the two surely only one can represent the actual facts. If from a false hypothesis no conclusion could be drawn, we would have to know which hypothesis is true before we could draw any consequences, but the drawing of consequences would be entirely unnecessary. The actual procedure of physical science does assume that hypotheses and consequences are bound together by strict laws, even when the former is false; otherwise it could not pass from the (factual) falsity of the consequences to the falsity of the hypotheses. Pure mathematics and symbolic logic simply confine themselves to the study of these implications, and the distinction between the actual and the possible can have no meaning in pure mathematics. Hence also pure mathematics must be allowed to enjoy a certain autonomy or relative independence of physics, which, indeed, our author sometimes admits (e.g., p. ix) although this admission is, of course, inconsistent with his refusal to admit a valid distinction between pure and applied mathematics and the kinds of truth involved in each (p. 453).

The alleged breakdown of the logistic philosophy leads to the final stage, the philosophy of intuition, on the basis of which our author elaborates his own philosophy of mathematics—the final book (Book VII) being entitled "Mathematical Intelligence and Truth." As, however, he claims this philosophy to be the direct result of history it is well to examine the methodological ideas which underlie this attempt to found a philosophy of mathematics on history.

To the idea that history can enable us to solve the perplexing problems of our own day, M. Brunschvicg joins the related but distinct idea that the history of mathematical science is necessary to make the philosophy of mathematics intelligible. Now there can be no doubt that in order to understand the various mathematical philosophies of history we must know the character of the mathematical science with which they had to deal. The opaqueness of the usual accounts of the Platonic, Cartesian or Leibnizian philosophies of mathematics by historians unacquainted with the history of mathematics amply illustrates this truth. The interests of historical understanding, however, are not always identical with those of doctrinal evaluation. In discussing historically a philosophy like the Kantian we need to know the ideas of the mathematics and mathematical physics of his own day, and the introduction of subsequent discoveries as to the adequacy or inadequacy of these ideas is likely to confuse our historical understanding. This point, at any rate, is insisted on in other fields of history.[2] Moreover, as M. Brunschvicg himself assumes, philosophers have not always kept in touch with contemporary science. Thus in spite of all the work in modern geometry, analysis, and mechanics, Neo-Kantians like Natorp still insist that we have *a priori* knowledge that space is Euclidean and that a non-Newtonian mechanics is forever impossible. The truth is that the problems of the philosophy of mathematics have always been profoundly influenced by general considerations arising from sources foreign to mathematical science, e.g., biology, ethics, etc. Hence M. Brunschvicg's thesis of a perfect parallelism between the "stages" of mathematical science and the "stages" of mathematical philosophy is not maintainable; and, as a matter of fact, it is seldom very useful.

The second idea, that historical study of itself can enable us to settle controversial problems, is, judging by the frequency of historical introductions to all sorts of axiologic discussions, one of the dominant ideas of our age. When one, however, examines these introductions they are found in most cases to be purely ornamental, or (in the case of writers who, like M. Brunschvicg, take their historicism seriously) they prove only those principles which their author has taken for granted in constructing his history. Indeed, how can anyone possibly organize a large tract of human experience in the way we call history without drawing on his own general ideas or philosophy? Even the doubtful argument that historical facts can speak for themselves could in no way be used here, for in this book we have no complete collection of all the facts, but, at best, a selection of what the author considers typical views.

The solidity of M. Brunschvicg's learning and his undoubtedly keen analytic powers make it rather instructive to note some of the confusion and self-deception to which he is led by the assumption that the history of a branch of philosophy

[2] See the Presidential addresses of Lea and Dunning before the American Historical Association, 1903, and 1913, in *American Historical Review*, 1904, and 1914.

can, apart from the direct analyses of the subject matter, prove anything as to the truth of contending views.

The idea of an instructive history of mathematical thought which presents "stages," obviously involves belief in something more than that a careful study of the great masters like Plato, Descartes, or Leibniz, is helpful. The latter kind of study need not be chronologic and is obviously futile unless accompanied by an independent vision of the subject matter. The idea of a history of doctrines which, apart from external reflection, can establish philosophic truth must rest on the belief that the time process represents a necessary logical development. It was brought into the history of philosophy by Hegel who consistently with his panlogism (i.e., all the real is rational) regards history as nothing but a logical unfolding. But though M. Brunschvicg does sometimes speak of certain doctrinal developments as necessary or inevitable owing to the nature of mind (e.g., p. 369), he is certainly not a conscious panlogist. His actual account of the development of mathematical thought, at any rate, has more dramatic elements than is possible with an Hegelian solitary actor who has to be his own antagonist and peacemaker. The course of mathematical thought has spontaneity; it exhibits a thousand accidents characteristic of a natural stream (pp. ix and 452); there have been false starts in the direction of dogmatism since the seventeenth century; great insights like those of Pascal (pp. 429, 439) have long been neglected; there have been unaccountable mental accidents like materialism (p. 307); and, worst of all, the prosperity or persistence of a doctrine is admitted to be no argument for its truth or falsity (p. 342). What doctrinal significance, therefore, remains to the historical order as such? From the standpoint of doctrinal truth must not Leibniz or Plato be judged like contemporaries? (cf. p. 397).

It is, I suppose, perfectly natural and proper for a philosopher, especially one who writes an historical introduction to his views, to characterize his own thought as the final stage

[255]

or great consummation toward which all creation has moved. But how about the previous stages? Are no crumbs of partial truth to be doled out to the former for their services? In spite of the assertion that the originality of the new stage consists in that it does not wish to add a new system of mathematical philosophy, but "turning to history itself, it seeks the convergence and co-ordination of the results which have been obtained at different periods" (p. 463), M. Brunschvicg's attitude to all previous systems of mathematical philosophy is almost entirely negative. The great lesson which his history teaches him is that we must clear the ground of the *a priorism* which has always infected mathematical thought, and return to primitive innocence (p. 458). I have tried to show that his refutation of previous philosophers like Russell is flagrantly inadequate. But at best there can be nothing historical in the refutation of a philosopher who is still vigorously developing his thought. The whole futility of the pretensions of historicism seems to me to be admitted in the following passage, which I quote in the original lest my translation be suspected of interposing a distorting medium: *"Au contraire c'est à la condition d'avoir compris d'abord la science qui agit et qui s'étend sous nos yeux, que l'on pourra, éclairé par elle, restituer au passé ce qui a été sa vie et son actualité"* (p. 458).

When M. Brunschvicg characterizes the final or present stage of mathematical thought as based on intuition he is unnecessarily projecting the stages of his discourse into a cold and noncompliant world. He argues indeed that mathematics is but the last of the sciences to receive the refreshing and fructifying breath of intuition (pp. 434-437); but he adduces nothing worthy of the name of evidence to show that biologists or physicists have actually changed their methods in accordance with the philosophy of intuition. Nor is it clear how they can possibly do so until we are vouchsafed a more definite explanation of what the method of intuition really means.

I may interpose that I speak here not as a cold or unsympathetic critic. I have myself a sentimental attachment for a doctrine of intellectual intuition to cover the brute fact that we do apprehend intelligible relations that are not sense data, and to call attention to the important problem of immediacy in logic,[3] and I am therefore ready to bless and be comforted by everyone who comes to speak in the name of my beloved doctrine. But M. Brunschvicg's message completely eludes me.

Intuition is sharply contrasted with logical deduction (pp. 395-396). It is a mental zone not of sense activity or logical reasoning (p. 428), yet it also includes (sensory) spatial intuition and logical deduction (as his remarks on Klein and Descartes indicate, pp. 450-451). Thus, being neither sense nor logic and at the same time both, it is fittingly characterized as "the profound work of intelligence" (p. 451). Nobody is likely to object to intuition if the latter is defined as "a method appropriate to the specificity of the object" (p. 440), but the only consequence which M. Brunschvicg draws from this is that the method of intuition must replace that of mechanism in physics and biology. But the adherents of mechanism in the latter sciences may well claim that the methods of mechanism are precisely those which are adapted to the specificity of their subject matter.

In the actual development of the details of M. Brunschvicg's own mathematical philosophy the idea of intuition is replaced by the idea of creative intelligence as the key to all the concrete problems of mathematics. Numbers, etc., are viewed as mental creations, and the peculiar harmony or truth which we observe in the fact that the results of our reasoning hold true of nature, is due to the fact that reason and experience are but two stages of the same creative mind or intelligence. So far as this rests on the general doctrine

[3] Refer to my paper on the "Present Situation in the Philosophy of Mathematics," *The Journal of Philosophy*, 1911, constituting Book II, Chapter 1, of *Reason and Nature* (1931).

of idealism, it would take us far afield to attempt to discuss it here. I can merely call attention to the fact that the introduction of an omnipotent factor like mind or creative intelligence in no way removes such a problem as the contradictions involved in the notion of a class of all classes.

While in the historical portion of his work M. Brunschvicg is sometimes compelled to speak of accidents and failures in the progress of mathematical thought, in his expository book human intelligence seems to have smooth sailing and no resisting medium. Sometimes, indeed, he speaks of mathematical forms as approximations, but as there is no eternal truth outside of the process of intelligence, it seems impossible to answer the question, approximations to what? In the main the work of the creative intelligence resolves itself into a long game of solitaire.

The motive which leads M. Brunschvicg to this position is quite clear and instructive to follow. Starting with the dogma that all logic is "analytic," and the vulgar prejudice that it can in no way help to extend our knowledge, he draws a very sharp distinction between the order of creation or discovery and the order of logic or exposition. In his insistence, however, on the all sufficiency of the order of invention or discovery he forgets or treats with contempt the order of facts.

The facts of mathematical science, however, distinctly refute the assumption of the sterility of deductive procedure. M. Brunschvicg insists that logic comes after "the spontaneous work of genius," and can only consecrate a victory already won or register the defeat. But even so, the implication that such "consecration" or "registration" is completely useless in extending the field of mathematics is absurd, unless we accept the view that genius works most fruitfully when its ideas are most confused. To believe this is really to revive the ancient but pernicious superstition that only the raving and demented are divinely inspired.

I bring this long, ungracious, and perhaps unduly censorious review to a close with the cheerful admission that it gives but a scant indication of the rich content of instructive study and suggestive analysis packed into this volume. The whole volume is written, in the main, with that admirable lucidity and regard for the gist of the matter which is characteristic of the best French exposition. Though the account of mathematical thought becomes more inaccurate as it approaches our own day, the accounts of Descartes, Spinoza, Leibniz and Kant are admirable examples of that painstaking scholarship of which the Germans are still serving as models.[4] But as a positive contribution to the subject its usefulness seems to me vitiated by the naïve acceptance of many of the now fashionable views in philosophy that are really in no way the outcome of laboratory experience or mathematical investigation; and I have deemed it worth while to call attention in this review to the difficulties of at least three of these fashionable views, viz., (1) the belief that logic and reflective or "dogmatic" thought are useless or worse; (2) the disbelief in, or disregard of, the Aristotelian distinction of that which is prior for us from that which is prior in nature; and (3) the widespread delusion that we can dodge the responsibility of a direct examination of the facts of a situation by coming in through the back door of history. Whatever may be the vices of modern logistic philosophy of mathematics, its adherents have at least tried to keep in mind the canons of scientific proof, and to eschew the rhetorical appeals which tend to make philosophy an irresponsible affair.

4 Written in 1915.

THE LOGICAL FOUNDATIONS
OF THE EXACT SCIENCES

IN THE RELATION between philosophy and science periods of intimate *rapprochement* seem to alternate with periods of mutual distrust. Professor Natorp [1] suggests that the true interrelations between the two are lost sight of in periods in which each is developing along established lines, but come to light in those critical periods in which either is compelled to strike out into new lines. At any rate, it is well to note that the traditional distrust of metaphysics on the part of scientists has recently been rapidly disappearing. The radical reconstruction of physical theory necessitated by recent research has driven physicists into philosophy almost in spite of themselves.

The volume before us represents the effort of a certain school of philosophy to reinterpret the meaning of mathematics and mechanics. The orthodox Neo-Kantian movement, of which Herman Cohen is the Nestor, has always interpreted the Kantian metaphysics as the logical foundation of Newton's *Principia;* and of late the Marburg school, of which Cohen and Natorp are the leaders, and E. Cassirer in some respects a most brilliant ally, has been especially active in tracing in detail the logical structure of the mathematical and physical sciences. Professor Natorp has for the past twelve years been publishing a series of papers and booklets on the philosophy of mathematics, and the work before us is the definitive form of this Neo-Kantian philosophy of the exact sciences. In consonance with its aim to be a modern "Critique of Pure Reason," the book seeks to be constructive throughout and *streng wissenschaftlich* in the classic sense. Still, the author does not disdain, in passing, to show us the frailties of the Neo-Leibnizians who have recently been hammering at the

---

[1] Paul Natorp, *Die logischen Grundlagen der exakten Wissenschaften* (Leipzig, 1910).

Kantian philosophy of mathematics in the most merciless manner. We may, therefore, also regard the book as the Neo-Kantian counterblast to Russell's *Principles of Mathematics* or to Couturat's version of it.

Chapter I is devoted to the consideration of "The Problem of a Logic of the Exact Sciences." As Professor Natorp views it, the situation resembles very much the one that confronted Kant. On one side are the empiricists, represented by Kronecker and Helmholtz, and on the other hand the Neo-Leibnizian school of Frege, Russell, and others who would reduce mathematics to pure logic. Professor Natorp, like Kant, rejects both of these positions, holding fast to both the *a priori* and the synthetic character of mathematical knowledge. He does not, however, follow Kant in attributing the peculiar certainty of mathematics to an *a priori* intuition. Instead he bases it on the synthetic process of thought. This, of course, will appear to many as an abandonment of the distinctively Kantian attitude, and as opening the floodgates of Hegelian panlogism which was so foreign to Kant. Professor Natorp, however, while a professed and thoroughgoing idealist, is tenacious in his adherence to the transcendental method and to the distinction between analytic and synthetic thought.

Dismissing the empiricists as not even worthy of the courtesy of a refutation, our author introduces his own point of view through a criticism of the analytic or "formalist" school. The error of this view is traced to the "dogmatic" Aristotelian logic which proposes to define everything until we come to the indefinable and prove everything until we get to the undemonstrable. This in turn is based on the fundamental error of naïve realism which regards things as given in perception, and conceives the work of thought to consist in the analytic working over of the content of perception. In opposition Professor Natorp holds to the Kantian dictum: No analysis without previous synthesis. As we cannot observe this synthesis in action, it is attributed to a "primitive understanding" (p. 9). About the metaphysic of this primitive understanding, where, when, and what it is, e.g., whether it is an individual or universal mind, no revelations are made to us. The only thing the author is willing to tell us is that it is not in time, and is beyond the ken of the psychologists (*cf.* p. 99). The uncertainty in which we are left as to the whereabouts of this primitive synthesis, prevents us from understanding Professor Natorp's attitude to ordinary logic. On one hand he tells us that ordinary logic is analytic and cannot extend our knowledge. Like the microscope, it can widen the angle between the rays, but cannot increase their number. On the other hand, he admits that Frege, Couturat, and even Wolff and the older Leibnizians mean by analysis something which does extend our knowledge. Indeed he is forced to use his own example of the microscope and admit that that instrument can materially add to our knowledge.

The effort to find a starting-point for his logic gives our author—not to mention the reader—considerable trouble. The transcendental method consists in following presuppositions. But there are no presuppositions unless something is given. What *is* given? It cannot be the object of perception, for that is precisely the thing which it is the aim of knowledge to determine. After a long discussion, in which a great deal of emphasis is laid on infinite process, *genetisch* as opposed to *ontisch*, the *fieri* as opposed to the *factum*, we reach the conclusion that the problem of logic (i.e., the transcendental variety) is to find those presuppositions which are necessary to bring the *x*—the undetermined, but to-be-determined, object of experience—into complete determination. This complete determination, we are assured almost *ad infinitum*, can be reached only by an infinite process.

In the second chapter we have a modernized deduction of the categories. The dry bones of the Kantian framework receive a great deal of flesh and blood. In the end, however, they turn out to be our old friends the Twelve, marching in four groups of three each. If it were not for the fact that students at our colleges *do not* read German, this chapter could profitably be recommended to those who are reading Kant for the first time and who generally cannot grasp what these categories are about.

In the third chapter we have a deduction of the number concept and of the four rules of arithmetic. The first condition, we are told, for the understanding of number is not to have anything to do with given things, for the latter already presuppose number. We must deal with rules of thought. Thought consists in nothing but positing relations, and the terms between which the relations hold are subsequent to the positing activity. Thus there is built up a fundamental series from which the number series is deduced. The issue of priority between ordinal and cardinal numbers is settled by calling them correlative. The mooted question as to whether the idea of number is dependent on time and space is answered mainly in the negative. Professor Natorp, however, thinks he saves something of the Kantian position by insisting that the relation of *before and after* is the common basis of number as well as of time and space. In his analysis of the operations of arithmetic he follows Simon, without, however, fully subscribing to the latter's stark subjectivism. Natorp admits that it is not enough to call numbers mental objects. We must show how they help us to cognize objects.

The critical work in this chapter is, whatever one may think of the constructive part, decidedly unsatisfactory. There is no attempt to come to close quarters with Russell's or Whitehead's definitions of numbers or their operations. Frege is taken as typical of the whole school, and arguments are used against him which Russell specifically answers. Many readers, however, who cannot grow enthusiastic about the application of transcendental logic in this field, will agree with Professor Natorp in his insistence that not only are the so-called real numbers (i.e., surds) and fractions to be looked on as operations, but even the series of positive integers must be so considered.

Chapter IV is devoted to "Continuity and Infinity" and

Chapter V to "Direction and Dimension" as terminations of pure number. The modern account of infinity and continuity is accepted, but Professor Natorp remains loyal to Herman Cohen and insists on the notion of the infinitesimal. By means of this he builds up the idea of the *reality of something* which forms a transition from mathematics to mechanics. The specific criticisms of Russell against Cohen's use of the infinitesimal method are not directly answered. Indeed, so far as the Marburg school is concerned, the great work of Weierstrass might as well never have been accomplished.

Chapter VI is entitled: "Time and Space as Mathematical Structures (*Gebilde*)." In the discussion of time and space the author adheres, in the main, to the Kantian view. He would, however, change the Kantian order somewhat, and make time and space refer back to the categories of modality, relation, etc. The main point seems to be the insistence that time and space are more than number in so far as they give existential reference to that which otherwise would be purely mathematical.

In the discussion of geometry, Professor Natorp no longer contends, as he did a few years ago, that metric geometry cannot be subordinated to projective geometry; and he also seems to weaken somewhat in his hopeless stand that non-Euclidean geometry contradicts the fundamental axioms of the continuity and homogeneity of space. Logically, he reluctantly admits, non-Euclidean geometry is possible. He rejects it, however, on the philosophical ground that a space of more than three dimensions or of non-Euclidean constitution would lead to endless indeterminateness, and make existential reference impossible. Why a three-dimensional Riemannian space, or even a four-dimensional mechanics as recently sketched by Minkowski, should be considered any more indeterminate than Euclidean space or Newtonian mechanics, the present reviewer cannot understand. A friend, however, makes the perhaps irrelevant suggestion that no man over forty-five will ever admit the possibility of a system of geometry other than the one which he was taught when a boy.

The last chapter—perhaps the most interesting—is entitled: "The Temporo-spatial Order of Phenomena and the Mathematical Principles of Natural Science." In the discussion of the question of absolute time and space, Mach's arguments against Newton are easily turned around to fortify the Kantian position. Absolute time and space are not found *in* experience precisely because they are the very conditions which make experience possible. Mach's argument that absolute time and space are not real things and, therefore, of no practical importance, is met by the observation that in the same way nothing in our experience is absolutely one, yet the laws of arithmetic based on abstract numbers are assuredly of some practical importance. Natorp's criticism of Mach would have been more effective if the former were in a position to analyze the latter's conception of existence (in the assertion that only relative motion *exists*); but Natorp's own conception of existence is, like that of most philosophers, entirely vague. For the most part he holds existence to be equivalent to complete determination (*cf.* pp. 336, 338). As we are repeatedly told that the process of determination is infinite, it would seem that the *existence* of things is the one thing forever unattainable to us.

The remainder of the last chapter is devoted to an epistemologic deduction of the fundamental laws of mechanics. Newton's laws of motion, and even the principle of the conservation of energy, are all shown to be necessary on the principles of transcendental logic. It is not likely, however, that Messrs. Abraham, Lewis, Bucherer, and the others will take those proofs so seriously as to discontinue their labors in the direction of a non-Newtonian mechanics which should meet the facts of physics more adequately than does the classic mechanics.

In the last two paragraphs of the book we have one of the first attempts to determine the philosophic value of the

[265]

relativity theory of Einstein and Minkowski. There is, however, no attempt to discuss the point wherein this theory does most violence to traditional views, viz., its conception of what constitutes simultaneity.

The book before us is German in more senses than one. It is thorough and packed with information and close reasoning. The author has spent considerable labor on the great mathematicians—though one suspects that the intercourse has been too Platonic, i.e., chaste and unfruitful. Professor Natorp does not seem to know the English or Italian works on symbolic logic. He apparently has not read Russell's book on Leibniz; indeed, he has not read Russell's *Principles of Mathematics* with great care, if we are to judge by his references to Russell's views on analytic and synthetic judgments. There is also no reference to such French works on the theory of science as those of Picard or Duhem. There are, indeed, a few references to the German translation of Poincaré's *Science and Hypothesis,* but the fundamental thesis of that work is not dealt with. Indeed, from the point of view which looks upon the fundamental principles of mathematics as hypotheses justified only by the fact that they give us a coherent scientific system, a good deal of Natorp's work as to the foundation of these principles must appear as entirely uncalled for.

Two closely related methods are typified in this book, which are characteristic of classic Hegelian philosophy and which have caused the latter to fall into such sad repute. These are (1) the method of dealing with the implication of *concepts* (not to be confused with the implication of propositions), and (2) the covert appeal to the self-evident. These methods are due to the prevailing belief that the relation between any two ideas is a relatively simple affair, which does not, like the relation between natural objects, need elaborate investigation. It is one of the great services rendered by mathematics to have shown that the relation between ideas requires long and patient inquiry, in which we are to be especially on our guard against any appeal to the apparently obvious. In a question like the convergency of a series, that which most people would regard as obvious turns out after laborious investigation to be almost invariably wrong.

We must, however, agree with Professor Natorp that there is much less danger today of Hegelian intrusions into the special sciences than there is of ignoring the fundamental problems of philosophy and of substituting for them an easy mixture of propositions from biology or physics seasoned with logically loose and vague general reflections. Such seem to me Ostwald's *Naturphilosophie,* and, in large measure, a good deal of the work of Avenarius and Bergson.

THE ORIGINS
OF MODERN SCIENCE

Pᴿᴼᶠᴱˢˢᴼᴿ Tʜᴏʀɴᴅɪᴋᴇ'ꜱ ʙᴏᴏᴋ [1] is one to delight those who
still value thorough scholarship, to comfort those who
despair at the way myths about the origin of "modern"
science are still taught in high places, and to tantalize those
who like to see history organized without loose ends around
definite ideas.

At a time when so many American historians are bitten by
the temptation to write like journalists for quick popular
consumption, it is delightful to meet a writer who thinks it
necessary to go to manuscript sources instead of relying on
secondary authorities of high reputation. From the point of
view of the amount of scholarly labor, even when dealing
with printed but unavailable sources like Galen, Professor
Thorndike's work is of the kind that may be described as
monumental. It is certainly one of the very few recent historical productions in America that can be put beside Lea's
History of the Inquisition.

The title of this book is somewhat misleading if it suggests
that the author's interest in experimental science is co-ordinate with his interest in magic. The latter is the primary and
larger object of research, and the former is only a sort of by-
product, not at all receiving the same completeness of treatment. Nevertheless, to philosophic readers it may be the more
valuable part, especially in challenging the prevailing myth
that theology and scholasticism prevented the growth of
science until Francis Bacon led the way to freedom by experiment and induction. Not only are we shown many
medieval writers preaching and practicing observation of
nature and experiment, but the account of Albertus Magnus

[1] Lynn Thorndike, *A History of Magic and Experimental Science
during the First Thirteen Centuries of Our Era* (Macmillan Company,
New York, 1923).

indicates that the great leader of scholasticism evidenced a juster observation of nature in subjects like botany and physical geography than the Bacon of whom Harvey said that he wrote science like a lord chancellor! The exaggerated claims, also, of Roger Bacon, as the pioneer of "modern" science and the story of his persecution on that account, are corrected wth discrimination and real fairness. Roger Bacon is seen as undoubtedly a great figure in the history of science, but somewhat petulant and jealous, and in many respects his views were not as just or "advanced" as those of much earlier scholastics like Adelard of Bath (see Vol. II, pp. 37-39).

But this is a subject on which a great deal more work has to be done, though Professor Thorndike's book, if supplemented by the work of Pierre Duhem, shows the way.

The very full account of various forms of medieval magic and queer superstitions may readily flatter our own vanity and feeling of superiority. But in the concluding chapter Professor Thorndike lays down some wholesome cautions in this respect. "Ptolemy believed in astrology, and how many [contemporary] archaeologists and philologists and students of early religion, mythology, and folklore [and philosophers in general] there are who fail to observe his great law that one should always adopt the simplest possible hypothesis consistent with the observed facts." Not only in the field of dress and etiquette do we, too, have taboos, but in the procedure of modern scholars, in collecting outlandish but erudite-looking footnotes full of abbreviated formulae, we have a parallel to the formulae of medieval apothecaries and the jargon of ancient incantations. But I imagine the most effective answer would be an account of the magic of our own day, including not only Maeterlinck on the Ouija board, but eminent scientists like Sir Oliver Lodge and the various believers in the supernatural power of mediums like Mrs. Piper, and priestesses like Mme. Blavatsky.

The tantalizing feature of this book is the absence of any well-defined idea as to what is the essence or distinguishing feature of magic. To say that it includes "all occult arts and sciences, superstition and folklore," involves the inclusion of all sorts of empirical knowledge about the arts of agriculture, medicine, etc., which are ignored by Professor Thorndike. Of course, an historian has the right to select any arbitrary number of beliefs, such as those in divination, astrology, alchemy, and the interpretation of dreams and, calling them all magic, proceed to write their history. But this makes his work a chronologic but disjointed catalogue of opinions on diverse, more or less related, topics. Indeed, any history of opinions which cuts itself off—as does Professor Thorndike's—on one side from the practical manifestation of these opinions in communal life, and on the other from any internal bond which connects these opinions, must remain essentially disjointed and fragmentary. This does not detract from the value of Professor Thorndike's work in bringing so much material to the foreground. But it indicates that an adequate interpretation of the material is not to be expected of it. Thus we are left without any increased understanding of such amazing careers as that of Apollonius of Tyana or of such striking facts as that Plotinus, who glorified the life of reason as above the power of magic, became the patron saint of Neo-Platonic superstition.

In the last chapter Professor Thorndike does, indeed, attempt a theory as to the origin of magic: "Men have a natural tendency to assert and craving to hear the sensational, exaggerated, and impossible, to fly in the face of both reason and experience. People take pleasure in affirming the extravagant and in believing the incredible, in saying that they have seen or done what no one else has seen or done" (p. 975). But while this points to an important factor which anyone can verify in the daily newspapers, it is clearly but partial and inadequate. Many beliefs in magic are obviously rationalizations of ritual (or motor) tendencies having their basis in organic processes. Just as the belief in the power of prayer arises primarily not from the observation of its objective efficiency, but from certain psycho-physical needs which the prayer itself meets, so the origin of the sympathetic magic that is supposed to bring about rain, injury to enemies, etc., is to be sought in the organic satisfactions which the ritual affords. There is no evidence for Professor Thorndike's view that "primitive" man intoning an incantation is utterly indifferent to its musical or esthetic quality.

All this is important for the purpose of this book in that it enables us to see what Professor Thorndike fails to indicate, viz., the general distinction between magic and experimental science. If we start with undeveloped empirical knowledge of the arts of agriculture and medicine, there is no basis for a distinction between natural science and supernatural magic, between swallowing the bark of the cinchona tree or wearing an amulet. Both may be fortified by empirical coincidences (remembering that negative instances do not produce as impressive effects as positive instances do). But as we develop bodies of coherent and respectable doctrines we call those beliefs magic and unscientific in which there seems (from our point of view) no rational connection between the act or ritual and its expected consequences. To pray for rain or victory is magic to one who believes in a naturalistic system, but it seems natural to those who regard divine intervention at request as similar to human response. (In communities where our systematic natural science is unknown its place is occupied by respectable or authoritative knowledge as administered by official priests, so that magic is generally illegal or disrespectable. The church which believes in miracles thus proscribes magic.)

Some such view, at any rate, is necessary to explain the presence of so much of what seems to us now such outrageously nonsensical beliefs in the minds of men of such acute intelligence and scientific insight as those treated in this book. Professor Thorndike offers an ingenious theory as to why magical beliefs continue in seventeenth-century manuscripts. But a careful reading of the early printed volumes of the *Transactions of the Royal Society* will show that what seem to us now magic was not absent among the colleagues of Boyle and Newton. Hegel's dictum that magic is to be found in all countries and ages is literally true.

There are several minor comments which seem to me worth making as to the execution of this book. An historian may, of course, begin at any arbitrary point of time. But the assertion that the beginning of the Christian era has any special significance for the history of magic or science is not justified. Only very slight, superficial, and perfunctory relations between Christianity and magic or science are indicated. On the other hand, Professor Thorndike does scant justice to the continued influence of pagan religious mysteries, or to the Democritean-Epicurean tradition as represented in Lucretius and Hero of Alexandria. His treatment of Arabic science and medicine is very inadequate (witness his omission of the Encyclopedia of the Brothers of Sincerity). He cuts himself off from a full understanding of the matter by ignoring the Syrian philosophers and physicians who constitute the bridge between Greek and Arabic science. Professor Thorndike is undoubtedly right in maintaining that some medieval works of real value were wrongly credited to Arabic authors. But the very existence of such a practice shows the high authority which Arabic works enjoyed. In general, the treatment of the history of medicine is unsatisfactory through failing to note the naturalistic philosophy implicit in the medieval tradition since Hippocrates. The treatise of Paul of Aegina, unjustly dismissed as a "wretched compilation" by Dr. Singer and passed over lightly by Professor Thorndike, shows the vitality of this naturalistic tradition in the very "dark" age of the seventh century. While it is perfectly just to insist that the Greeks of the classic age were not free from magic, it seems to me absurd to suggest that their reputation for sober rationalism was given to them by the men of the Renaissance, by men like Pico della Mirandola who wallowed in cabalistic lore. Also, while the treatment of Peter of Abano is most admirable, full justice is not done to his tremendous influence. While there is little actual Averroist medicine in his great treatise, it is a fact that within a generation after his death he became a sort of patron saint of the Averroist tradition in medicine, against which Petrarch (anticipating Bernard Shaw) waged a ridiculous war.

Finally, I should like to point out that while it is a great service to call attention to the scientific culture of men like Pliny and Ptolemy, the suggestion that the latter *must have been* a greater astronomer than Hipparchus is not historically justified. It rests on an *a priori* belief in universal progress, with which the history of science in the centuries following Archimedes and Hipparchus does not agree.

But these are minor points in a book of indispensable importance for the history of the great adventure which we call human thought.

INDEX

ate Due